To Grandmother at Christmas
time —
Susan

Guide to American Pewter

I

GUIDE TO
AMERICAN PEWTER

Carl Jacobs

Illustrated by Marion B. Wilson

THE McBRIDE COMPANY, INC.
New York, N. Y.

Library of Congress Catalog Card Number: 56-12017

Acknowledgments

First, I would like to express my appreciation to Dr. Ledlie I. Laughlin, whose *Pewter in America* is, in my opinion, one of the most scholarly and comprehensive works in any field of American antiques. Then to those two men who charted this most unfamiliar field before him, J. B. Kerfoot and L. G. Myers, all pewter enthusiasts are greatly indebted; also to Charles F. Montgomery, Director of the Henry Francis Du Pont Winterthur Museum, formerly a dealer in pewter, who stepped in and created a market when general interest was flagging. Many fine pieces were saved from oblivion, or worse, the scrap heap, through his untiring efforts.

I wish to thank Dr. A. C. Abbott; C. K. Davis; W. Deckelman; Mr. and Mrs. Oliver Deming; J. J. Evans; Reginald French; Eric DeJonge; William G. Goss, Jr.; H. J. Kauffman; C. J. McCarthy; J. H. McMurray; John Ruckman; A. S. Sherry; Marion B. Wilson; Miss J. Wolcott; and many others, for their valuable and scholarly comments. Dr. Dean A. Fales, Jr., has helped in the revisions and listings of this book. Most photographs are by the Ray Robinson Studio, Westfield, Massachusetts.

CARL JACOBS
Southwick, Mass.

Contents

Preface.. 13

Collecting Pewter.. 17

Check List of American Pewterers...................................... 21

Appendix
    The Danforths of Connecticut...................................... 201
    Characteristic Pewter Forms... 207

Illustrations

1. A sweetmeat dish by Francis Bassett I 30
2. A group of forms by the Bassetts 31
3. A range of plates and beakers 35
4. Tankards by Philadelphia makers 35
5. Two very rare porringers by William Bradford
   and William Kirby 46
6. Rose-and-crown touch of Thomas Byles 50
7. Small basin porringer by Edward Danforth 51
8. Normal touches of John Danforth 63
9. Porringers by John Danforth and Josiah Danforth 68
10. Rear view of Danforth porringers 69
11. Rare tankard by Samuel Danforth 73
12. Mark on Samuel Danforth tankard 74
13. Plates and mugs by Samuel Danforth and the Boardmans 75
14. Rampant-lion touch, probably of Thomas Danforth I 75
15. Rampant-lion touch, probably of Thomas I and John Danforth 75
16. Normal touches of Thomas Danforth II 77
17. Porringer by Thomas Danforth II or Thomas Danforth III 78
18. Tankard by Benjamin Day; plate by Thomas Byles 83
19. Basin and plate by John Dolbeare 86
20. Seventeenth-century platter attributed to John Dolbeare 89

21. Marks on platter attributed to John Dolbeare..............90
22. The mark of John Dolbeare, Sr...............90
23. New England tankards by Day, Danforth, and "IC" or "IG"...........100
24. Pennsylvania pewter..............100
25. Teapots by "H.J.", Danforth, and Boardman..............108
26. Combination touch on teapot by "H.J."..............108
27. A varied group of chalices and beakers..............110
28. Porringers, by Gershom Jones and Henry Will..............116
29. Southern pewter..............118
30. A range of basins..............118
31. A group of rarities, by "HG", Leddell, "DS", and Horsewell............124
32. Rare spoon by Richard Lee..............124
33. Quart tulip-shaped tankard by "Love"..............130
34. Teapot in Queen Anne style by "Love"..............131
35. All excellent forms, mostly eighteenth century, unmarked............141
36. Marked porringers showing diversity of handles..............148
37. "Semper Eadem" Boston touch with "London" scroll..............154
38. "I.S." rose-and-crown touch with "Semper Eadem"..............155
39. Boston Pewter..............160
40. Normal flatware touches of John Skinner..............167
41. Rhode Island anchor touch on plate by Tillinghast..............168
42. Group of pieces by Dunham, Endicott & Sumner, Pierce, Richardson, Dolbeare, Trask, Lee, Yale, Gleason, and Hopper..............170
43. Two tall flagons by Henry Will..............177
44. Group of pieces by the Wills..............181
45. Two tankards, by John Will, Jr. and John Will, Sr...............183
46. Three Philadelphia tankards, by Cornelius Bradford and William Will..............187
47. New York City and Albany pewter; chalices by Peter Young..........187
48. "Middletown" scroll touch used by Thomas Danforth II and Amos Treadway..............192
49. Mark of Peter Young..............193
50. Pewter by the Danforths and the Boardmans of Connecticut............202

Appendix Illustrations

51. (a) Crown handle, New England and New York. (b) Conventional "Old English," New England and New York. (c) Flowered, Rhode Island and Connecticut. (d) Geometric, New England and New York..............207

52. (a) Solid, Rhode Island type. (b) Solid, Pennsylvania type. (c) Dolphin, New London and Hartford. (d) Lee-type four-handled basin, unique..............208

53. (a) Lee-type double-handled basin, unique. (b) Handle unique to Lee. (c) Also unique to Lee..............209

54. Lee-type handles: (a) Also used by Boardman. (b) Unique to Lee. (c) Also used by Gleason. (d) Unique to Lee. (e) Also used by Isaac C. Lewis. (f) Unique to Lee. (g) Unique to Lee. (h) Unique to Lee, raised pattern..............210

55. (a) Handle unique to Lee. (b) Boardman type. (c, d, and f) Lee types. (e) New York type..............212

56. Characteristic tea and coffee pot shapes: (a) Globular, Love bird touch. (b) Pear-shaped; the Wills, Cornelius Bradford, and Brunstrom. (c) Rudimentary foot on pear-shaped; Richardson and others. (d) Pear-shaped; William Calder and others. (e) Footed pear-shaped; William Will and Cornelius Bradford. (f) Federal style with feet; Israel Trask and others. (g and h) Federal style, circular and oval; William Will, George Coldwell, Parks Boyd, and others..............214

57. (a) Pear-shaped, footed base; Richard Lee, Brunstrom and others. (b) Tall; many makers. (c) Coffee pot; William Will. (d) Tall; Samuel Danforth, Thomas D. Boardman, Samuel Kilbourn, and others. (e) Pigeon-breasted; Gleason and others. (f) Type from mid-nineteenth century; by Reed & Barton..............216

Preface

As an introduction, I am going to quote from two noted authorities on pewter. First, the late Professor Percy G. Raymond, for many years editor of the Pewter Collectors' Club *Bulletin,* remarked disparagingly on "those monomaniacs who collected only American pewter." Dr. Ledlie I. Laughlin observed that over-zealous collectors, in their determined search for such a prestige item as an American tankard, overlooked the much rarer and equally desirable contemporary teapots—eighteenth century ones, of course.

There are many important forms, such as measures, which either do not occur in American pewter, or if they do, are one or two of a kind, and so rare and so highly priced, that only a few collectors can hope to own one. Any collector of average means, striving to achieve a well balanced collection, would be foolish to reject an English example. Indeed, the range of forms in English measures will intrigue any but the most narrow minded collectors. You can have a lot more fun for your money and attain better intrinsic value by recognizing that form and mark are equally important. Continental examples offer equal opportunities for collectors who seek excellence of form and usability.

Many collectors seek, and rightly, either pewter for decoration, or use. It is sheer folly for people of modest means (and that includes most of us) to insist on marked items for such purposes. Many of the best forms in American pewter occur both marked and unmarked. Examples are six- and eight-inch basins, plates of all sizes, small and large beakers, and church pewter, including flagons and chalices. In many instances only one or two pieces of a communion set are marked. Unmistakably American forms, such as Boston strap-handle pint mugs and Philadelphia sugar bowls of the eighteenth century, almost always are unmarked.

Many other forms, which have been found marked, may be bought unmarked cheaply. Perhaps the most desirable and valuable of these are the William Will ewers, flagons, and tankards. The very rare Heyne chalices usually are not marked. These pieces are worth well into the hundreds; unmarked six-inch plates (true rarities in American pewter) can still be bought for about twenty dollars.

For every marked American porringer, there are several unmarked counterparts to be had for a fraction of the price of marked ones. This is also true of mugs, tankards, and nearly every form imaginable, many of which can be definitely assigned to a known maker.

Guide to American Pewter

Collecting Pewter

We who live in the mid-twentieth century eat from porcelain, and lately, plastic tableware. It is difficult for us to conceive the dominant role of pewter ware on the tables of our ancestors for more than two hundred years after the settlement of this country, and abroad for generations before that. With the exception of isolated frontier villages which were dependent on their own hewn or turned wooden (treen) ware and a few wealthy families in the coastal regions who used silverware, pewter and earthenware were used universally. Infants sucked milk from pewter bottles and spooned pease porridge from pewter porringers The table board was set with pewter basins, plates, and platters.

Pewter and bronze, of the same alloy in inverse ratio (nine to one) of the metals tin and copper, were fabricated by the ancient Chinese, Egyptians and Romans. Their use was probably contemporaneous and undoubtedly goes back beyond the dawn of history. Though lately, in terms of centuries, antimony and bismuth have supplanted copper, the formula before 1700 was nine parts tin to one part of copper. In hollowware and, on the part of unscrupulous makers, in flatware, lead was often introduced in varying proportions.

In addition to tableware, such diverse household and personal articles as lamps, candlesticks, chandeliers, furniture hardware, buttons and buckles were of pewter. This universal metal was of equal importance to iron; its use probably surpassed that of brass and copper. In an isolated village the pewterer was perhaps only a tinker, mender, and spoon caster. In the larger communities he was a respected artisan and an essential member of the community. Many were prominent in local and even national affairs. To those of us who collect pewter, the part played by certain of these men in helping create our country is often an important factor in the desirability of their products. It is regrettable that the raw-tin embargo, placed on this country by England whose rulers wished to export only the finished metal, forced our early pewterers to rely largely on scrap pewter for the melting pot. This accounts for the dearth of pre-revolutionary marked American specimens today. The history of pewter making in this country is as old as that of the settlement of the English colonies. Each small settlement had, if not a working pewterer, at least someone who owned a spoon mold, either individually or collectively, to recast broken or worn-out articles into usable ones. There were several pewterers working in the Massachusetts Bay settlements in the 1630's. Joseph Copeland is known to have been a working pewterer in Chuckatuck and Jamestown, Virginia, as early as 1675. The country was growing rapidly; there was a steady demand for pewter ware of all sorts. Few families were so poor or isolated that they could not afford at least several pieces to complement their wood and pottery; few were rich enough to own any silver, and that was used in those days only on special occasions.

Though pewter is a soft metal and its life short even with careful usage, worn or damaged articles could always be brought to the pewterer and recast into shining new forms. The basis for pricing pewter was always weight, and the customer could receive about two-thirds of the value-weight of his scrap pewter in new.

Thus it would seem that the opportunities for an emigrant pewterer in a new expanding land were limitless. But there were many obstacles to a successful pewtering career. The nearest source of the principal raw material, tin, was three thousand miles away, and travel was slow and uncertain. It needed little urging from the powerful guild of London pewterers to make the mother country virtually prohibit the export of raw tin to the colonies. It was the deliberate policy of England, right up to and even after the Revolutionary War, to force the colonies to accept exports of manufactured goods and to keep the colonies dependent on her.

After a long apprenticeship, a man wanting to set up shop on his own, would first have to buy, build, or rent a shop. Benches, lathes, hand tools, cauldrons, and forges had to be bought. The most expensive items were the numerous brass molds for casting various forms. The cost of these alone would run to several thousand dollars in present day currency. Mainly because of this, though partly to supplement their income, nearly all colonial pewterers were also braziers. Some were also plumbers and ship chandlers for items in lead. Many sold hardware, usually imported. Nearly all sold English pewter as well as their own products. For casting their own ware, they were utterly dependent upon, and limited by, the amount of scrap pewter they could obtain. For every one that succeeded, there were many that failed, and many who never became more than journeymen working for other pewterers.

During the past thirty-five years, thousands of pieces of American pewter have been bought and sold. It seems worthwhile to establish stabilized market prices for the bulk of this pewter. It should be recognized that there are many unmarked items, of American manufacture, that bring very good prices indeed. Some collectors prefer the English or Continental pewter for their often superior quality or diversity of form.

Prices quoted are based on a number of factors which are listed below. They are retail prices, for items in fine condition with clear touchmarks. This must be remembered at all times. For pewter with pitted or scaly surfaces, or these conditions in conjunction with worn touchmarks, and for pieces with more than very minor repairs made or needed, deduct from one to two-thirds of listed prices. Prices listed here are for the perfect piece, though it may exist only hypothetically. Do not expect dealers to pay full retail prices. Some pewter is both early and scarce, yet worth little; demand governs prices, as in any field of antiques. In some instances prices are necessarily estimates, there being no record of actual sales.

In these listings, various terms denote comparative scarcity: common or plentiful, scarce, rare, and unique. These designations are purely relative, however. For example, the pewter of Thomas Danforth, II, of Middletown, Connecticut, is listed as plentiful. While it is rare in comparison to the output of some of the later britannia makers, it is plentiful when compared with examples by some of his contemporaries, such as Amos Treadway or Jacob Whitmore of Middletown. Yet it is far less common than that of the Boardmans, working later, who are placed in the same category. Similarly, some examples by makers of the britannia period are very rare, yet their pewter is not necessarily valuable. Demand determines price and pieces held in little value today may bring higher prices tomorrow.

The following factors govern value:
1. Date of manufacture. Pre-revolutionary items are true rarities.
2. Style. Unusualness or beauty of form is always important.
3. Condition of pewter and touch marks.
4. Rarity of maker or form.

5. Usefulness or desirability of form. Porringers are relatively common but one of the most sought after items; they lend themselves to display or use. Cuspidors are real rarities, and go begging.
6. Historical interest. Many pewterers, such as Gershom Jones, Cornelius Bradford, and William Will, played prominent parts in the Revolutionary War.
7. Technical construction. In flatware, for example, plates with smooth brims or hammered booges bring premiums.
8. Regional origin. Items made south of Baltimore, even after 1800, hold a special interest for some collectors, aside from their rarity.

It should be remembered that prices of pewter, as for any commodity, are subject to fluctuation from time to time. They follow general economic trends and rise and fall with interest in collecting. The discovery of additional pieces bearing the mark of a pewterer whose work is scarce will decrease prices of previously discovered pieces.

In many instances, especially in flatware, a spread in prices is given. Most pewterers had several different touches; their rarest or earliest (and they often are the same) bring the highest prices. While general trends are established in pricing American pewter, there are always exceptions which should be noted. For particulars of the various touches, their makers, dates and comparative scarcity, see J. B. Kerfoot's *American Pewter*, or for more comprehensive and recent information, Ledlie I. Laughlin's *Pewter in America*.

This book, although primarily a price guide, also includes concise information that will be useful to collectors and dealers. Every known touch mark is illustrated as well as every type of porringer handle. More than ninety percent of the porringers found in this country, in contrast to plates, are of American origin, whether marked or not. Contrary to popular belief, there are almost no distinctively American porringer handles. There are English or Continental prototypes for most.

Listed are many American makers, whose work has been found and not recorded in any previous book. Hundreds of hitherto unrecorded forms and many new touches are also listed, as is information concerning new working dates or the locale of a pewterer. Such new information is indicated by an asterisk (*) placed before the pewterer's name or the article. The illustrations of forms occurring in successive periods, as in tea and coffee pots for example, should prove a useful guide in determining their age and value.

In many instances, it will be noted that no values are given for some sizes of flatware or forms under certain touches. This indicates an unrecorded form. To leave such spaces open will give the reader a better clue to rarity than to estimate a value. Some of these unknown combinations of form and touch are now reposing in collections or private homes and may be recorded later. Others will perhaps never turn up.

Where makers worked in the britannia period, from about 1825 on, they are so designated. A few, like the Boardmans of Hartford, beginning in 1805, worked right through the britannia period and never made anything but pewter. Others, like Gleason and George Richardson, spanned the periods and made both.

Generally speaking, britannia and pewter are not so much different alloys as methods of manufacture. Pewter was cast in a mold; britannia was turned on a wooden form on a lathe. Although many desirable forms occur after 1825, nevertheless the introduction of the new method marked a general deterioration in design. After 1825, the earlier forms, plates, mugs, tankards, and porringers, were infrequently made. The emphasis fell on tea and coffee pots, lamps and candlesticks. Wherever possible, exact sizes of marks are illustrated. Marks on britannia, being chiefly straight-line name touches, are not shown in this book.

ADAMS, HENRY W., New York City, 1857. Rare.
    Britannia Lamp   35.00

ALBERTI, JOHANN PHILIP, Philadelphia, 1754-1780.
No known examples.

ALBERTI and HORAN (Philip Alberti and Johann Christian Horan), Philadelphia, 1758-1764.
No known examples.

ALLAIRE, ANTHONY J., New York City, 1816-1821.
No known examples.

ALLISON, ANDREW, Philadelphia, 1837-1841.
No known examples.

ALLISON, JOHN, Philadelphia, 1835-1836.
No known examples.

*APPLEBEE, J., probably New England or Albany district, 1820.
    15″ platter, rectangle name touch, unique   400.00

ARCHER, BENJAMIN, St. Louis, 1847.
See ARCHER and JANNEY.

ARCHER, ELLIS S., Philadelphia, 1842-1850. Rare. Britannia.
    Lamp, as to style   15.00—25.00

ARCHER and JANNEY (Benjamin Archer and N. E. Janney), St. Louis, 1840-1850. Scarce. Britannia.

Lamp   25.00

ARMITAGES and STANDISH, eastern Massachusetts, 1840's. Britannia.

Tea Pot   30.00
Sugar Bowl   25.00

AUSTIN, JOHN, Boston, 1785.
No known examples.

AUSTIN, NATHANIEL, Charlestown, Massachusetts, 1763-1800. Plentiful. This maker is best known for his flatware, as are most eighteenth-century pewterers. With the exception of spoons, of which almost no early examples have survived, the eight-inch plate was the form most commonly made by the early pewterer; it is the basis of many collections today.

(1)   (2)

(3)   (4)

*7½″ plate,
rare size   (3)   75.00
8″ plate   (2) 200.00   (3)   45.00   (4) 40.00
8⅝″ plate   (3)   50.00   (4)   45.00
8¾″ plate   (1) 250.00   (3)   45.00   (4) 37.50
*8¾″ plate,
(smooth brim) eagle
and hall marks   (3) 175.00
9½″ plate,
(smooth brim)   (2) 300.00
9¾″ plate,
(smooth brim)   (1) 300.00   (2) 300.00
12″ plate   (3)   85.00   (4)   85.00
12″ plate,
(smooth brim)   (3) 250.00   (4) 250.00
13½″ plate,
(flat)   (3)   75.00   (4)   70.00
13½″ plate,
(deep)   (3)   85.00   (4)   80.00
15″ plate (flat)   (3) 150.00   (4) 135.00
8″ basin   (3)   95.00   (4)   85.00
9″ basin   (3) 125.00   (4) 115.00

(5)

Quart mug with strap handle; circular name
touch at base of handle   (5) 350.00

AUSTIN, RICHARD, Boston, 1792-1817. Plentiful. Richard was a distant relative of Nathaniel's. Though he worked later, his pewter is scarcer but far from uncommon. The curved name touch is the latest and rarest. He is known to have shared a shop with Samuel Green, for a time, but no combination touch is known. With many of Richard Austin's pieces size is approximate. Three sizes in 8″ range are found. His small 7¾″ plates, with extremely narrow brims, are made from an early mold and are worth twenty percent more than the prices below.

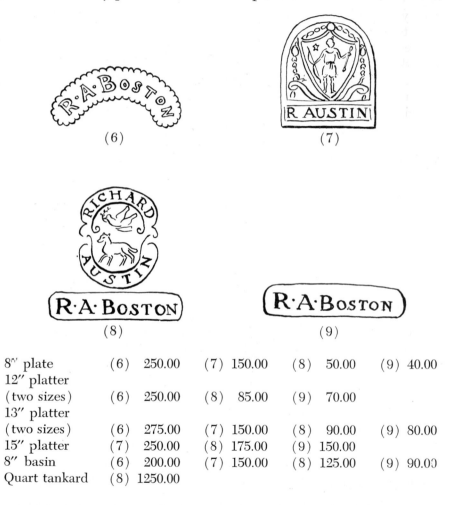

(6)   (7)

(8)   (9)

8″ plate	(6)	250.00	(7)	150.00	(8)	50.00	(9)	40.00	
12″ platter (two sizes)	(6)	250.00	(8)	85.00	(9)	70.00			
13″ platter (two sizes)	(6)	275.00	(7)	150.00	(8)	90.00	(9)	80.00	
15″ platter	(7)	250.00	(8)	175.00	(9)	150.00			
8″ basin	(6)	200.00	(7)	150.00	(8)	125.00	(9)	90.00	
Quart tankard	(8)	1250.00							

B., R., (with rose & crown), probably Boston, middle to late 1700's. Rare. There is uncertainty as to the user or users of this touch. It was once thought that Robert Boyle, a New York City pewterer, had moved to Boston; yet this seems unlikely, as no trace of him can be found there. This touch has been found in conjunction with the "Boston" and "London" scrolls used by other Boston pewterers, and also with the "Semper Eadem" touch. Possibly the original user was Robert Bonning, who could have made the tankard and church cups listed, and possibly the tulip shape mug; yet he worked too early to have made most of the items that have come to light. There is a record of a sale to a New Hampshire church of tall beakers bearing this touch in 1796. It is doubtful if it was used any later than this. Regardless of whether the originator was a Bonning, a Boyle, or a Byles, it seems that from about 1750 on, the touch was used as a trademark by a succession of pewterers, such as Skinner, Nathaniel Austin, or Green.

(10)

8″ plate	125.00
9″ plate	150.00
11⅞″ plate, rare size for Boston	250.00

Flatware bearing the "Boston" or "London" scrolls is worth fifteen per cent more than the above prices, while pieces bearing the "Semper Eadem" touch are worth twenty-five per cent more.

6″ basin	185.00
8″ basin	150.00
5″ beaker	250.00
Church cup, unique in American pewter	1000.00 or more

(Undoubtedly made by a pewterer trained in London, lending credence to the Bonning attributions.)

Church Cup, two handled   1000.00 or more
Pint mug, tulip shaped   350.00
Pint mug, straight sides   400.00
*Quart mug, strap handle   450.00
*Quart tankard, tulip shape, with finial   2000.00
5½″ porringer, unique   600.00

BABBITT and CROSSMAN, Tauton, Massachusetts, 1814-1828. Scarce.

Tea and coffee pots   25.00 to 35.00
Small britannia beaker   35.00
Inkstand (a rare form in marked American pewter)   75.00
*4⅛″ round mirror frame,
with firm name on label. Very rare.   125.00

BADCOCKE, THOMAS, Philadelphia, 1710.
No known examples.

BADGER, THOMAS, Boston, 1737-1815. Plentiful. Though this man's
father is thought to have been a pewterer, no piece that has been identified as the work of the senior Badger has been found.

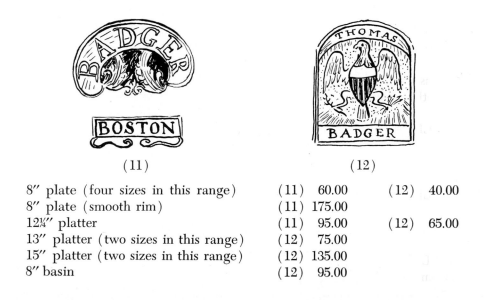

(11)   (12)

8″ plate (four sizes in this range)   (11) 60.00   (12) 40.00
8″ plate (smooth rim)   (11) 175.00
12¼″ platter   (11) 95.00   (12) 65.00
13″ platter (two sizes in this range)   (12) 75.00
15″ platter (two sizes in this range)   (12) 135.00
8″ basin   (12) 95.00

BAILEY, TIMOTHY, Malden, Massachusetts, 1830-1840.
See BAILEY and PUTNAM.

°BAILEY and BRAINARD, Cobalt, Connecticut. About 1840.

    Communion set, unique   200.00

BAILEY and PUTNAM (Timothy Bailey and James H. Putnam) Malden,
Massachusetts, 1830-1835. Rare. Britannia.

    Tea and coffee pots   25.00 to 35.00
    Lamp   25.00

BAKER, JOHN, Boston, 1676-1696. Very rare.

(13)

°17″ semi-broad brim plate with multiple reed rim; hammered
booge and brim.   750.00

This is one of some half-dozen seventeenth-century Boston plates extant.
For other examples with similar marks, see the Dolbeares.

°BALDWIN, D. S., Connecticut, 1850. Britannia. Rare.

    Britannia tablespoon   8.00

°BALDWIN, L. G., Meriden, Connecticut, 1849. Britannia. Rare.

    °Britannia tablespoon   8.00

BALL, WILLIAM, Philadelphia, 1775-1782.
No known examples.

BARNS, BLAKSLEE, Philadelphia, 1812-1817. Plentiful. The rectangle name touch, the only one in which Barnes is spelled with an "e," and the small circular name touch, are worth thirty-five percent more.

(14)

(15)

6⅛" plate	(15) 175.00	
8" plate (two sizes in this range)	(14) 55.00	(15) 35.00
9" plate (two sizes)	(14) 60.00	(15) 40.00
9¼" plate (smooth brim)	(15) 150.00	
11" deep dish	(15) 50.00	
13" deep dish	(15) 65.00	
6⅝" basin	(15) 125.00	
8" basin	(15) 45.00	
9" basin	(14) 75.00	(15) 60.00
10" basin	(15) 75.00	
*10" basin, hammered	(15) 150.00	
13" basin, rare size	(15) 175.00	

BARNES, STEPHEN, Middletown or Wallingford, Connecticut, 1791-1800. Rare.

(16)

7⅞″ plate	150.00
8¾″ plate	175.00
11⅛″ deep dish	195.00
13″ deep dish	225.00

BARTHOLDT, WILLIAM, Williamsburg, N. Y., 1850-1854. Scarce. Britannia.

Candlesticks, pair	65.00

BARTON, CHARLES E., (partner in Leonard, Reed, and Barton), Taunton, Massachusetts, 1835-1860.
See LEONARD, REED, and BARTON.

BASSETT I, FRANCIS, New York City, 1715-1740. Extremely rare. Only a few specimens definitely attributable to this maker are known. It is probable that some of the touches listed under Francis II are those of

*Fig. 1: A sweetmeat dish (diameter 8½") by Francis Bassett I, dated 1728.
A form virtually unique in American pewter.*

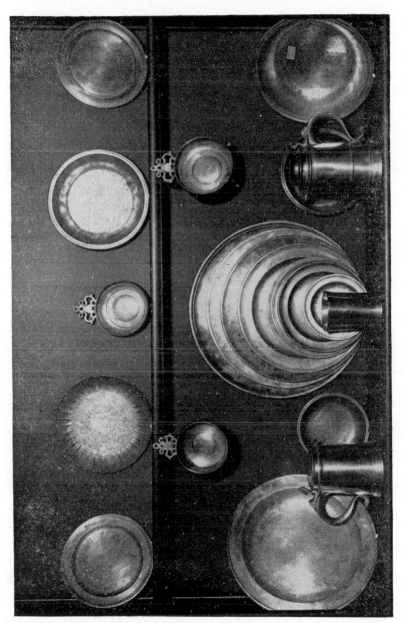

Fig. 2: A group depicting most known forms made by the Bassetts of New York. Examples pictured are by Francis Bassett I, Francis Bassett II, John Bassett, and Frederick Bassett. Notable are the dated sweetmeat dish (top row, second from left), the only other known example of which is shown in Figure 1, and the 3½-pint tankard (bottom row, second from right)—an extremely rare size, with the fish-tail handle.

Francis I as well. All the Bassetts were craftsmen of unusual ability. Their products command higher prices than comparable pieces by most of their contemporaries. A dish by Francis Bassett I is shown in Figure 1.

(17)

(18)

8½″ plate

*8½″ plate, fluted and engraved, dated in 1720's

*9¼″ plate, smooth brim, hammered booge

(18)   350.00

(17) 1000.00 or more

(18)   450.00

BASSETT II, FRANCIS, New York City, 1749-1800; except for *1780-1783, Caldwell and Montclair, New Jersey. Rare.

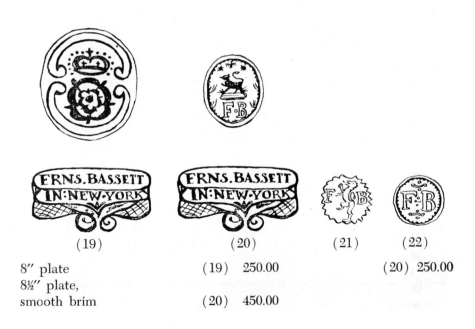

(19)   (20)   (21)   (22)

8″ plate   (19)   250.00   (20) 250.00
8½″ plate,
smooth brim   (20)   450.00

9" plate	(20)	300.00
*9" plate,		
smooth brim	(20)	450.00
16" deep dish	(19)	900.00
Porringer	(21)	650.00
8" basin	(21)	400.00
5⅝" beaker	(21)	600.00
Pint mug	(21)	500.00
Quart mug	(21)	550.00
Quart tankard	(21)	2000.00
3-pint tankard	(21)	2500.00

(22) 700.00

BASSETT, FREDERICK, New York City and Hartford, Connecticut, 1761-1800. Scarce.

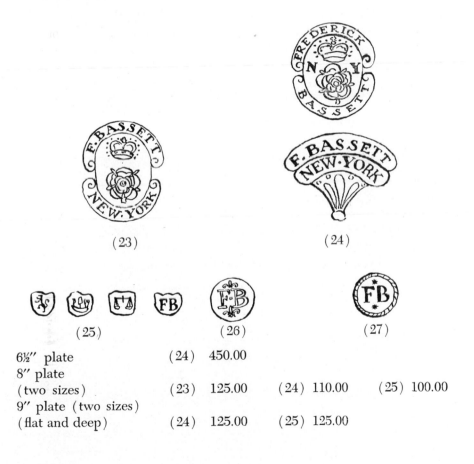

(23)

(24)

(25)

(26)

(27)

6½" plate	(24)	450.00			
8" plate					
(two sizes)	(23)	125.00	(24)	110.00	(25) 100.00
9" plate (two sizes)					
(flat and deep)	(24)	125.00	(25)	125.00	

9¼″ plate (smooth brim)	(23)	300.00	(24)	275.00	(25)	275.00
12¼″ platter	(24)	175.00	(25)	175.00		
13⅜″ platter	(24)	225.00	(25)	225.00		
*13″ deep dish	(24)	225.00	(25)	225.00		
15″ platter (two sizes)	(23)	300.00	(24)	300.00	(25)	300.00
16⅝″ platter	(23)	500.00				
(Platters over 16″ are very rare.)						
6¼″ basin	(24)	325.00				
8″ basin	(24)	200.00				
10¾″ basin	(24)	275.00				
*Tablespoon, coffin end	(27)	300.00				
Pint mug	(26)	400.00	(27)	400.00		
Quart mug	(26)	400.00	(27)	400.00		
Pint infusion pot	(27)	1000.00				
4¼″-5″ porringers	(26)	500.00	(27)	500.00		
5⅝″ beaker	(27)	500.00				
Funnel	(27)	650.00				
Nursing bottle	(27)	700.00				
Commode form	(27)	700.00				

Frederick Bassett also made seven distinct types of tankards, in three-pint and quart sizes. Prices for these range upwards from one thousand dollars, depending on the style.

BASSETT, JOHN, New York City, 1720-1761. Very rare.

(28)

(29)

*4⅞″ porringer	650.00
6¾″ beaker	800.00
Quart tankard	2000.00
3½ pint tankard	3000.00
9″ basin	275.00
10½″ basin	400.00
Funnel	850.00
Slip top spoon	400.00
Dram flask	1000.00

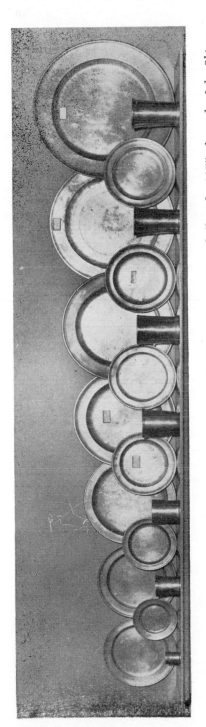

Fig. 3: A range of plates and beakers. The plates range from the 5¾" by Samuel Campbell to the 16⅝" platter by John Skinner. Beakers: 1½" New England, unmarked; 2⅝" by Thomas Wildes; 3" by Samuel Danforth; 4¼" by I. Trask; 4⅞" by Frederick Bassett; 5" by Samuel Danforth; 5⅞" by Edward Danforth.

Fig. 4: Tankards by Philadelphia makers. Left to right: "Love," Parks Boyd, Cornelius Bradford, "Love," and William Will.

BEACH, Chester, Connecticut, 1837.
See RUSSELL and BEACH.

*BECK, JOHN VALENTINE, Pa., and Winston-Salem, North Carolina, 1731-1791. Possibly only a spoon caster.
No known examples.

BECK, THOMAS, Trenton, New Jersey, third quarter of the eighteenth century. Britannia. Rare.

    Spoon   8.00

BEEBE, St. Louis, 1840.
See SAGE and BEEBE.

BELCHER, JOSEPH, and BELCHER, JOSEPH, JR., Newport, Rhode Island, and New London, Connecticut, 1769-1784. Rare. Except in the instances where the "New London" touch is added, the products of these two men are indistinguishable.

            (J:B)   {N.LONDON}
             (30)   (31)

*6″ plate	(31)	450.00
8″ plate	(31)	150.00
*9⁷⁄₁₆″ plate, smooth rim, (New London)	(31)	300.00
*11³⁄₁₆″ dish	(31)	250.00
13″ deep dish (two sizes)	(31)	250.00
4″ porringer, unusual open handle	(30)	450.00
5″ porringer, flowered handle	(30)	375.00
5″ porringer, solid handle (two sizes)	(30)	450.00
5″ porringer, crown handle	(30)	375.00
8″ basin	(31)	250.00

BENEDICT, LEWIS, Albany, New York, 1815-1824.
See STAFFORD, SPENCER.

BENHAM, MORRIS, West Meriden, Connecticut, 1849. Britannia.
No known examples.

BENHAM and WHITNEY, New York City, 1850. Britannia.
No known examples.

BIDGOOD, Philadelphia, 1825.
See PLUMLY and BIDGOOD.

BILLINGS, WILLIAM, Providence, Rhode Island, 1791-1806. He worked for a time in partnership with Job Danforth, Jr. No joint touch, nor any attributable to the latter, has been found.

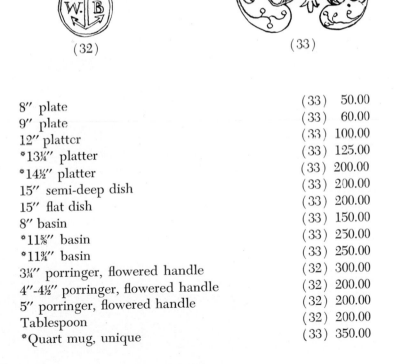

(32) (33)

8″ plate	(33) 50.00
9″ plate	(33) 60.00
12″ platter	(33) 100.00
*13¼″ platter	(33) 125.00
*14½″ platter	(33) 200.00
15″ semi-deep dish	(33) 200.00
15″ flat dish	(33) 200.00
8″ basin	(33) 150.00
*11⅝″ basin	(33) 250.00
*11¾″ basin	(33) 250.00
3¼″ porringer, flowered handle	(32) 300.00
4″-4½″ porringer, flowered handle	(32) 200.00
5″ porringer, flowered handle	(32) 200.00
Tablespoon	(32) 200.00
*Quart mug, unique	(33) 350.00

BIRD, JAMES, New York City, 1820.
No known examples.

BLAND, JAMES, Westchester County, New York, 1760.
No known examples.

BLIN, PETER, Boston, 1757-1759.
No known examples.

BOARDMAN, HENRY S., Hartford, Connecticut, and Philadelphia, Pa.,
1841-1861. Very scarce.

BOARDMAN
PHILADA

(34)

5½″ tall beaker   125.00

BOARDMAN, J. D., Hartford, Connecticut, 1828.
No known examples.

BOARDMAN, LUTHER, South Reading, Massachusetts, and Chester,
Connecticut, 1836-1842. Later, this man and his sons made britannia
and plated spoons in East Haddam, Connecticut.

(35)   (36)

Teapot, various shapes	(35)	35.00
Teapot, late pear-shaped		
(small base extension)	(35)	150.00
Teaspoon, various styles	(36)	7.00
Tablespoon, various styles	(36)	10.00

BOARDMAN, THOMAS DANFORTH, and partners, Hartford, Connecticut, 1805-1850. Plentiful. This man and his relatives were very successful pewterers. Their output, together with that of their relatives, the
Danforths, accounts for over one-half of the surviving American pewter.
Their work was of uniformly fine quality and, with the exception of
some later forms, of good design. Some of their pewter was marked
"N. York," where they had a sales office, but all was made at Hartford.

Touches include large and small eagle name touches, a straight line name touch with "Hartford" worth a twenty-five per cent premium, a TDB rectangle touch worth twenty per cent more than listed prices, and a TD&SB in rectangle. There are at least three variants of this last touch, yet they may be considered as one in terms of value. Later touches include "BOARDMAN and HART," and "HALL, BOARDMAN & CO.," the latter used for their Philadelphia sales outlet. These last two, as well as their lion touch, were used from the 1830's onwards.

Though some premium should be given to the rectangle initial touch of T.D.B., the "Hartford" touch, and the early eagle touches, for the most part the value is in the form rather than the mark. The number of forms they made was so enormous, that in flatware, for example, only typical examples are listed.

(37)   (38)   (39)

(40)   (41)   (42)

T.D.BOARDMAN   X   BOARDMAN
HARTFORD   T.D.B.   N-YORK
                                                        & HART
(43)   (44)   (45)

X   BOARDMAN
BOARDMAN   & HART
& HART
N·YORK   N-YORK   BX𝖜
(46)   (47)   (48)

*6³⁄₁₆" plate		125.00
6½" plate		100.00
8" plate		30.00
7¾" plate, TD&SB and eagle		40.00
8⅛" plate, smooth brim, TD&SB with double eagles		125.00
8¾" plate, TD&SB		40.00
9" deep plate		40.00
*10¾" deep dish		50.00
12" flat plate, smooth brim		125.00
13" deep dish		60.00
6½" basin		90.00
8" basin		50.00
9" basin		60.00
12" basin		125.00
14" basin		400.00
14" basin, with cover		650.00
Large ladle	25.00	embossed 80.00
Small ½-gill mug	35.00	marked 125.00
½-pint mug		195.00
Pint mug		160.00
Quart mug		160.00
Quart mug, but massive; actually a lidless tankard		300.00
Quart tankard		450.00
Quart tankard, with pour spout		250.00

13″ Communion flagon, with double C handle and 3-tier finial		125.00
14″ communion flagon, S D type, flare base		250.00
Communion flagon, but plainer form		95.00
Same Communion flagon, but late type with lion mark		60.00
*Two handled mug or church cup, pint,		75.00
	quart	325.00
3″ beaker	plain,	35.00
	with mug handle	60.00
4″ beaker, with reinforcing mid rib, straight sides		75.00
5″ beaker		95.00
6¾″ beaker, with mug handle		90.00
Chalice, always unmarked	single	30.00
	pair	75.00
Baptismal bowl, footed		125.00
Covered sugar bowl		45.00
Lamp, ship's swivel		45.00
Lamp, various styles as to form and size	each	25.00— 35.00
Teapot, pear-shaped		135.00
Teapot, with large base extension transitional form		200.00
Miniature teapot		75.00
Teapot, drum-shaped		200.00
Later type teapot, on form		20.00— 40.00
Tall coffee pot, often with engraved band		45.00
Open balustre measure, 18th c. style, ½-pint to 2-quart		150.00—200.00
2-quart water pitcher	open	45.00
	covered	75.00
3-quart water pitcher	covered	95.00
Gallon water pitcher	open	125.00
	covered	150.00
5-quart water pitcher	open	150.00
	covered	200.00
Cream pitcher, from pint mug mold		75.00
Water pitcher, japanned, with the Edward Danforth hallmarks		350.00

Japanned pieces are extremely rare in American marked pewter. The few examples of Boardman touches accompanied by the Edward Danforth hall marks are rare and should bring a fifty per cent premium over the prices listed. This is true also of BX quality mark.

Porringer, Old English handle, three types, various sizes	60.00— 75.00
Porringer, crown handle, various sizes	60.00— 75.00
Porringer, flowered handle	90.00—100.00
Porringer, simple triangular type handle by T.D.B.	85.00
Inkwell	200.00
Bedpan	75.00
Nursing bottle	150.00
Chamber candlesticks, saucer base, pair	100.00

BOARDMAN, TIMOTHY & CO., New York City, 1822-1824. Scarce. Timothy was either a partner of, or a manager for, T. D. & S. Boardman.

X

(49)

½-gallon measure	275.00
3″ beaker	45.00
5″ beaker	95.00
Nursing bottle	175.00
*Pint mug, rare	225.00
*Quart mug, rare	225.00
Teapot	65.00

BONNING, ROBERT, (or Bonnynge) Boston, early 18th century. This pewterer may have been the original user of the "RB" rose and crown touch which has been found in conjunction with both "Boston" and "London."

Yet the items thus far turned up which bear this touch would be too late for him, with the possible exception of church cups and other hollow-ware. (*See* "B., R.")

BOUIS, JOHN & JOSEPH, Baltimore, Maryland, 1830's. Britannia. No known examples.

BONZIGUES, Philadelphia, early 1800's. No known examples.

*BOWDITH, "CAPTAIN," Salem, Massachusetts, 1814. This man is reported to have made Federal oval teapots and Communion sets.

BOWLES, SAMUEL, Boston, late 1700's. No known examples.

BOWMAN, NATHANIEL, Charlestown, Massachusetts, early 1800's. No known examples.

BOYD, PARKS, Philadelphia, 1795-1819. Scarce. Boyd's pewtering is of the highest order, showing, as does the work of William Will, Philadelphia craftsmanship at its best.

(50)   (51)   (52)

6″ plate		(51)	300.00	(52)	275.00
8″ plate (two sizes)	(50) 85.00	(51)	75.00	(52)	70.00
*8½″ plate, smooth brim	(50) 250.00				
9″ deep dish	(51) 90.00	(52)	75.00		
9½″ plate, smooth brim	(51) 250.00	(52)	225.00		
11″ deep dish	(51) 135.00	(52)	115.00		
12½″ deep dish	(50) 125.00				
13″ deep dish (two sizes)	(50) 165.00	(52)	135.00		

*5¹⁵⁄₁₆″ basin	(51)	250.00
6½″ basin	(51)	200.00
Pint mug	(50)	250.00
Quart mug	(50)	250.00
Quart mug, barrel-shaped	(50)	450.00
Quart tankard, plain	(50)	1200.00
Quart tankard, with light ribbing, (same mold as "Lovebird" examples)	(50)	1400.00
*Quart tankard, with pour spout	(50)	800.00
Quart tankard, Swedish style, heavy ribbing	(50)	1400.00
Covered pitcher	(50)	250.00
Covered round box	(50)	300.00
*Covered sugar bowl	(50)	400.00
*Teapot, drum-shaped	(50)	450.00

BOYLE, ROBERT, New York City, 1752-1758. Very rare.

(53)

9″ plate   600.00

BRADFORD, CORNELIUS, New York City, 1752-1753 and 1770-1785; Philadelphia, 1753-1770. Scarce. This maker emigrated from England. In keeping with old country tradition, he used his master's hallmarks. A few plates have turned up bearing these "DS" hallmarks in conjunction with a "London" rose and crown touch, indicating that Bradford, like Skinner and others, had "London" pewter for those who wanted this quality. This conjunction of marks is very rare and should bring an additional premium of fifty per cent, or more.

(54)   (55)

8½″ plate	(54)	250.00		
8¾″ plate	(55)	200.00		
9″ plate	(55)	250.00		
9″ plate-hammered booge	(55)	400.00		
9¹⁵⁄₁₆″ plate, smooth brim	(55)	450.00		
Pint mug	(55)	450.00		
Quart tankard	(54)	1600.00	(55)	1600.00
*Teapot, footed and pear-shaped	(55)	2500.00		

BRADFORD, JOHN, Boston, 1784-1788.
No known examples.

BRADFORD, WILLIAM, JR., New York City, 1719-1785. Very rare.

(56)   (57)   (58)   (59)

*9″ plate	(58)	600.00
Circular box, an extremely rare form in American pewter	(58)	850.00

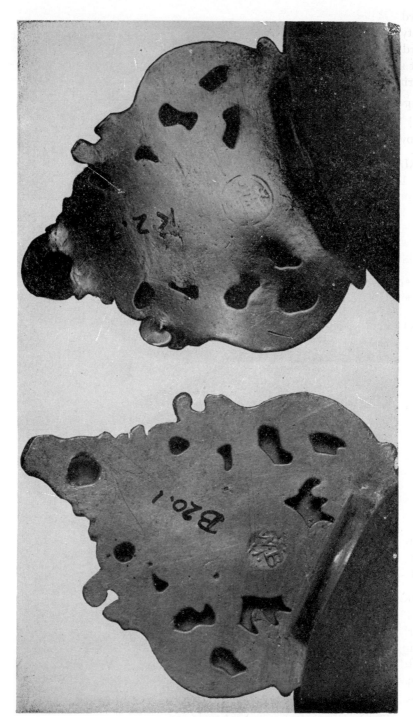

Fig. 5: Two very rare mid-eighteenth-century New York porringers by William Bradford and William Kirby.

Tankard, domed top,
early style   (56) 2000.00   (59) 2000.00
Tankard, flat top,
earliest style   (57) 2250.00
4" porringer   (56)   500.00

BRADFORD and McEUEN, (Cornelius Bradford and Malcolm Mc-
Euen), New York City, 1772-1785.
No known examples of this partnership.

*BRAMAN, ELIJAH, Taunton, Massachusetts, and Warren, Rhode
Island, 1834-1839. Rare. Britannia.

BRAMAN

(60)

    *Castor   35.00
    *Teapot   35.00

BRICKLEY, T. M., Troy, New York, 1835. Rare.

    *Lamp   35.00

BRIGDEN, TIMOTHY, Albany, New York, 1816-1819. Rare. His mark
is sometimes found in conjunction with the marks of S. Stafford, indicating that Brigden, like Peter Young, at times worked for Stafford.

(61)

Communion chalice, single   450.00   pair 1200.00
Flagon   1000.00
Teapot, late pear-shaped   400.00

BROOK FARM, West Roxbury, Massachusetts, 1841-1847. Very rare.
Brook Farm was one of the prominent community-living experiments of
the early nineteenth century, comparable to the ones at Oneida, New
York, and New Harmony, Indiana. For that reason, its pewter commands
prices far beyond its intrinsic merit.
    Employee pewterer was Ephraim Capen of CAPEN and MOLY-
NEUX, which see.

(62)

Lamp, tall   single 60.00   pair 150.00
Teapot   50.00

BROOKS, DAVID S., Hartford, Connecticut, 1828.
No known examples.

*BROOM, JAMES, Ogles-town (New Castle), Delaware, 1748.
No known examples.

BROWE and DOUGHERTY, Newark, New Jersey, 1845. Britannia.
No known examples.

*BROWER, A., New York City, 1820. Rare.

   *Candle mold—pewter tubes, marked, in wood frame,
  unique   65.00

BRUNSTROM, JOHN ANDREW, Philadelphia, 1783-1793. Rare. As
more of Brunstrom's pewter comes to light, collectors have discovered
that he was not just another country pewterer, but a maker of high
ability. Much of his flatware is hammered. Although his craftsmanship
is below that of William Will and Parks Boyd, he is, nevertheless, one
of the major Pennsylvania pewterers.

(63)

  *6″ plate   350.00
  *8″¼″ plate, smooth brim   300.00
  *10½″ plate, smooth brim   350.00
  *12⅛″ platter (sometimes appears with
  hammered booge)   250.00

*6″ basin	300.00
8″ basin	225.00
*9⅛″ basin	250.00
*11⅜″ basin	300.00
*11¾″ basin	300.00
*12¼″ basin	350.00
Pint mug	400.00
*Quart mug	450.00
5³⁄₁₆″ porringer, tab handle	400.00
*Pear-shaped teapot	2000.00

BUCKLEY, TOWNSEND M., Troy, New York, 1854-1857. Rare. Britannia.

Lamp   single, 30.00 . pair 70.00

BULL, LYMAN, and COUCH, Meriden, Connecticut, 1845-1849. Britannia.
No known examples.

BUMSTEAD, THOMAS, Roxbury, Massachusetts, 1640-1643; Boston, 1643-1677.
No known examples.

BURDETT, AARON, Baltimore, Maryland, early 1800's. Rare.

(64)

8″ plate   250.00

BYLES, THOMAS, Newport, Rhode Island, 1711-1712; Philadelphia, 1738-1741. Note the similarity of the forms listed in Byles' inventory and those made by "RB." That would seem to place "RB" in Newport, but the conjunction of "RB" marks with those of Boston pewterer, J. Skinner, would still be unresolved.

Fig. 6: The rose-and-crown touch of Thomas Byles who worked in Newport as early as 1711, as found on an 8½″ plate. Byles also worked much later in Camden and Philadelphia.

*Fig. 7: Rare small basin porringer, marked in well
by Edward Danforth of Middletown and Hartford.
Late eighteenth century.*

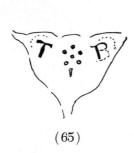

(65)

(66)

*5″-5⁷⁄₁₆″ porringer, geometric handle, (earliest known marked American porringer)	(65)	1000.00
8″ plate, hammered booge	(66)	350.00
8¼″ plate, smooth brim, hammered booge	(66)	400.00
9″ plate	(66)	400.00
*10⅞″ plate, hammered booge	(66)	500.00

C., E., probably New England, 1800. "EC" is one of the mysterious unidentified marks found on the backs of porringers.

*4½″ porringer, Old English type handle   75.00

*C., I., New England, probably Boston, 1725-1760. These initials have been found cast in the handles of two styles of tankard of patently eastern New England origin. Some have a barrel handle terminal, while others have an embryonic bud terminal. Some have finials, while others do not. One of these tankards, without this mark, is known to have been used in the early 1730's, while another from the same mold was made by Richard Austin. Thus, the mold was in use for a long period of time.

*Quart tankard, marked   1200.00
*Quart tankard, unmarked   400.00

CAHILL, J. W. & CO., location unknown, 1830's. Rare.

Teapot   45.00

CALDER, WILLIAM, Providence, Rhode Island, 1817-1856. Plentiful.

(67)

(68)

8″ plate		(67) 45.00
8⅜″ plate, scarce size		(67) 55.00
*9½″ plate, smooth brim, rare		(67) 150.00
11″ deep dish		(68) 35.00
8″ basin		(67) 60.00
10″ basin		(67) 90.00
Flagon	(67) 125.00	(68) 100.00
Chalice		(68) 35.00
Teapot, pear-shaped		(67) 150.00
Teapot, pigeon-breasted		(68) 45.00
Teapot, later styles		(68) 25.00
3″ beaker		(68) 45.00
Candlesticks, pair		(68) 85.00
Lamps, pair		(68) 75.00
Small sparking lamp		(68) 35.00
Porringer, flowered handle, 4″ range		(67) 145.00
Porringer, flowered handle, 5″ range		(67) 145.00
Pint mug, rare		(67) 225.00
Handled cup		(68) 45.00
*Baptismal bowl, top diameter, 10⅞″. Base diameter 5⁷⁄₁₆″		(68) 250.00

Known to have made 6″ plates—none extant.

CALVERLEY, JOHN, Philadelphia, 1840's.
No known examples.

CAMP, WILLIAM E., Middletown, Connecticut, 1850.
No known examples.

CAMPBELL, JOHN, Annapolis, Maryland, 1749-1770.
No known examples.

CAMPBELL, MUNGO, Philadelphia, 1750's.
No known examples.

CAMPBELL (CAMPMELL), SAMUEL, Connecticut, early 1800's. Very
rare.

(69)

5″ plate   300.00
8″ plate   150.00

CAPEN and MOLINEUX; CAPEN, EPHRAIM, New York City, 1848-
1854; Dorchester, Massachusetts, *1844-1847. Plentiful.

Lamp, as to style and size   15.00—30.00
Lamp, swivel   45.00
*Cigar lighter   75.00

CARNES, JOHN, Boston, 1723-1760. Extremely rare and early.

(70)

7½″ plate, narrow brim, semi-deep   350.00
*Quart tankard, with finial   2500.00

CARTER, SAMUEL, Boston, 1712-1747.
No known examples.

*CASEY, GIDEON, Providence and S. Kingston, Rhode Island, 1726-1786. Extremely rare. He is the only American silversmith known to have made pewter.

G CASEY

(71)

*5″ porringer, crown handle   650.00

CINCINNATI BRITANNIA CO., Cincinnati, Ohio, 1850. Rare.

Ladle   60.00

CLARK(E), JONAS, Boston, 1715-1737.
No known examples.

CLARK(E), THOMAS, Boston, 1674-1720.
No known examples.

*CLUNN, MATHEW, Trenton, New Jersey, 1769.
No known examples.

*COLBURN, H. R., Location unknown, 1830. Rare. Britannia.

*Lamp   25.00

COLDWELL, GEORGE, New York City, 1787-1811. Rare.

G.COLDWELL

(72)

Dessert spoon, engraved	250.00
Tablespoon, engraved	250.00
Small oval box	350.00
Snuff box, japanned, very rare	450.00
3½" beaker, japanned and engraved	450.00
*Teapot, boat-shaped	450.00
*Teapot, drum-shaped	450.00
*Ladle	250.00

COLTON, OREN, Philadelphia, 1835-1836. (*See also* WOODBURY, J. B.) Rare. Britannia.

O. COLTON

(73)

Baptismal bowl	125.00

COMER, JOHN, Boston, Massachusetts, 1674-1721.
COMER, JOHN, JR., Boston, 1700-1706.
No known examples by either of these men.

*COMPAIRE, CLAUDIUS, Charlestown, South Carolina, 1736. Possibly a tinker only.
No known examples.

CONE, S. L., Meriden, Connecticut, 1850's.
No known examples.

CONNELL, THOMAS, Philadelphia, 1829-1840.
See PALETHORP, JOHN H.

COPELAND, JOSEPH, Chuckatuck and Jamestown, Virginia, 1675-1691.

(74)

One tablespoon has been uncovered, with the possible exception of the plates attributed to Baker and the Dolbeares of Massachusetts, the earliest surviving piece of marked American pewter. Evaluation of such a piece would be impossible.

CORNE, ANTHONY, Charlestown, South Carolina, 1735.
No known examples.

COTTON, *Middlefield, Connecticut, 1840's.
See HALL and COTTON.

COUCH, IRA, Meriden, Connecticut, 1830-1845.
See GRISWOLD and COUCH.

COWLES, GEORGE, East Meriden, Connecticut, 1834-1835.
See LEWIS and COWLES.

COX, WILLIAM, Philadelphia, 1715-1721. Extremely rare. Touch shown is that struck on London touchplate in 1710. Possibly this is the same man who later worked in Philadelphia.

(75)

*CREESY and LEE, Beverly, Massachusetts, 1815-1820. Rare. Probably a partnership of Creesy and Richard Lee, Jr.

LEE & CREESY

L&C

(76)

*Oval teapot, Federal style   350.00

*CROSSMAN, E. (Possibly Ebenezer), Taunton, Massachusetts, or Newport, Rhode Island, early 1800's. Extremely rare. Two plates recorded by the author. The striking resemblance of this man's touches to those of the Melvilles and Gershom Jones should be noted. There can be no doubt that the same die maker made all three. The size of the plates found are identical with a mold used by S. and T. Melville. Perhaps this man was the father of the Crossman listed below, or at least a relation.

(77)

*8⅝″ plate   350.00

CROSSMAN, WEST, and LEONARD, Taunton, Massachusetts, 1828-1830. Scarce. Britannia.

Teapot	25.00 — 35.00
Coffee pot	35.00
Tea set	125.00
Sugar bowl	25.00
Creamer	25.00
Flagon	85.00

CURTIS, EDWIN E., Meriden, Connecticut, 1838-1845. Britannia.
No known examples.

CURTIS, ENOS H., Meriden, Connecticut, 1845-1849. Britannia.
No known examples.

CURTIS, LEMUEL J., Meriden, Connecticut, 1836-1849. Scarce.
Britannia.

      Teapot   25.00

CURTIS, STEPHEN, New York City, 1858-1867.
See YALE and CURTIS.

CURTIS and CURTIS, (Edwin E. and Lemuel J. Curtis), Meriden, Connecticut, 1838-1840. Britannia.
No known examples.

CURTIS and LYMAN, (Lemuel J. Curtis and William W. Lyman),
Meriden, Connecticut, 1846. Britannia.
No known examples.

CURTISS, DANIEL, Albany, New York, 1822-1840. Scarce. Pewter and
britannia.

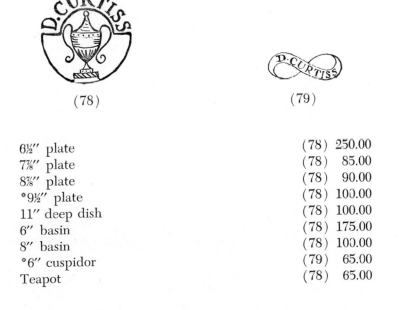

(78)   (79)

6½″ plate	(78)	250.00
7⅞″ plate	(78)	85.00
8⅞″ plate	(78)	90.00
*9½″ plate	(78)	100.00
11″ deep dish	(78)	100.00
6″ basin	(78)	175.00
8″ basin	(78)	100.00
*6″ cuspidor	(79)	65.00
Teapot	(78)	65.00

Teapot, pear-shaped	(78)	150.00
Coffee pot	(78)	85.00
Gallon water pitcher	(78)	200.00
*Pint mug, early form	(79)	225.00

A Curtiss of Bristol, England, made pear-shaped teapots. The mark is Neptune holding a trident in one hand and a dolphin by the tail in the other hand.

*CURTISS, F., probably Connecticut.

    *13¼″ ladle   65.00

CURTISS, I., Connecticut Valley, 1815-1820. Rare.

I.CURTISS

(80)

6″ plate	225.00
8″ plate	95.00
*6⅜″ basin	150.00

CURTISS, JOSEPH JR., Albany and Troy, New York, 1827-1859. No known examples.

CUTLER, DAVID, Boston, Massachusetts, 1730-1765. Extremely rare.

(81)

8¾" plate, hammered booge   450.00

*CUTLER, JAMES, Salem, Massachusetts, 1770-179?. Extremely rare.

*Sundial, with name and date   300.00

DANFORTH, EDWARD, Middletown, Connecticut, 1788-1790; Hartford, Connecticut, 1790-1794. Scarce.

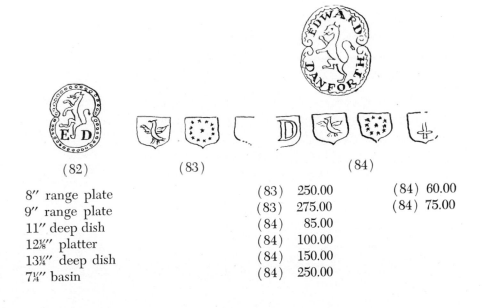

(82)   (83)   (84)

8" range plate	(83) 250.00	(84) 60.00
9" range plate	(83) 275.00	(84) 75.00
11" deep dish	(84) 85.00	
12⅛" platter	(84) 100.00	
13¼" deep dish	(84) 150.00	
7¼" basin	(84) 250.00	

*8″ basin   (82)   200.00
9⅛″ basin   (82)   225.00
5⅛″ beaker, very rare   (82)   450.00
3⅞″ porringer, marked in well,
basin type   (82)   400.00
4″ range porringer, two sizes,
Old English type handle   (82)   400.00
4″ porringer, marked in well   (82)   450.00
*5″ porringer,
flowered handle   (82)   500.00
Pint mug   (82)   350.00
Quart mug   (82)   375.00
*Quart tankard, very rare   (82) 2000.00

DANFORTH, HENRY G., probably Richmond, Virginia, 1830. Very rare. Oval name touch. Also reported to have put an eagle touch on his plates.

(85)

*Plate, 8″ or 9″ range   300.00

DANFORTH, JOB, Providence, Rhode Island, 1798-1801. He worked in partnership with William Billings. No touch for either Danforth or the partnership has been recorded, although a piece of pewter bearing the mark of Job Danforth was advertised for sale in the early 1940's.

Fig. 8: *The normal touches of John Danforth, found on flatware.*

DANFORTH, JOHN, Norwich, Connecticut, 1773-1795. Rare.
(*See* also THOMAS DANFORTH I.)

(86)

(87)

(88)

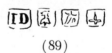

(89)

(90)

(91)

7⅞" plate	(87)	125.00	(90)	125.00			
8⁵⁄₁₆" plate	(87)	150.00	(88)	200.00	(90)	150.00	
*9⅜" plate, smooth brim	(90)	350.00					
*9⅜" plate, semi-deep	(89)	150.00					
12³⁄₁₆" plate	(86)	300.00	(87)	200.00	(88)	350.00	(90) 200.00
13¼" deep dish	(87)	250.00	(88)	85.00	(90)	250.00	
*4½" porringer, geometric handle	(91)	500.00					
*5¼"porringer, flowered handle	(91)	475.00					
5" range porringer, dolphin handle	(91)	450.00					
5" range porringer, crown handle	(91)	325.00					

Note striking resemblance to touches of Gershom Jones of Providence.

The 12³⁄₁₆" plate above with the Norwich scroll, lion in oval touch would seem to indicate that the Norwich rather than Middletown Danforths were the makers. The riddle of the accompanying Middletown hallmarks is unresolved.

DANFORTH, JOSEPH, Middletown, Connecticut, 1780-1788. Plentiful. This man worked with his father, Thomas II, from 1780-1782. His work is so plentiful for an early worker that we must conclude that his son, Joseph, Jr., used his father's touches and worked in Connecticut for some time before going to Richmond, where he made eagle-marked plates in the 1800's. (*See also* DANFORTH, JOSEPH, JR.)

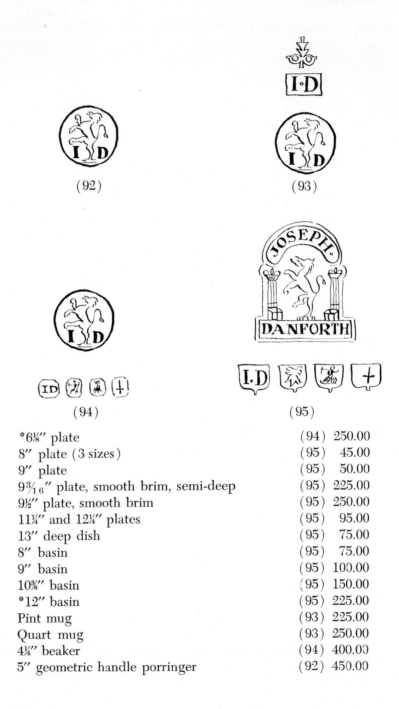

(92)

(93)

(94)

(95)

*6⅛″ plate	(94) 250.00
8″ plate (3 sizes)	(95) 45.00
9″ plate	(95) 50.00
9³⁄₁₆″ plate, smooth brim, semi-deep	(95) 225.00
9½″ plate, smooth brim	(95) 250.00
11¼″ and 12¼″ plates	(95) 95.00
13″ deep dish	(95) 75.00
8″ basin	(95) 75.00
9″ basin	(95) 100.00
10⅜″ basin	(95) 150.00
*12″ basin	(95) 225.00
Pint mug	(93) 225.00
Quart mug	(93) 250.00
4¼″ beaker	(94) 400.00
5″ geometric handle porringer	(92) 450.00

Mugs without the lion touch inside bottom are worth twenty percent less.

DANFORTH, JOSEPH, JR., Richmond, Virginia, 1807-1812. Extremely rare.

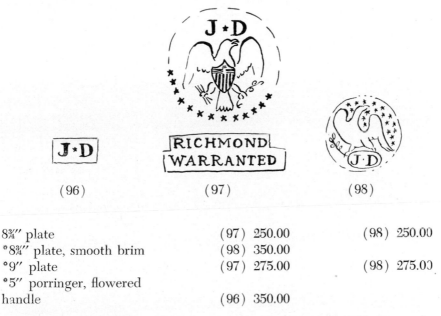

(96)   (97)   (98)

8¾″ plate	(97) 250.00	(98) 250.00
*8¾″ plate, smooth brim	(98) 350.00	
*9″ plate	(97) 275.00	(98) 275.00
*5″ porringer, flowered handle	(96) 350.00	

DANFORTH, JOSIAH, Middletown, Connecticut, 1825-1837. He made both pewter and britannia. Scarce in pewter; common in britannia.

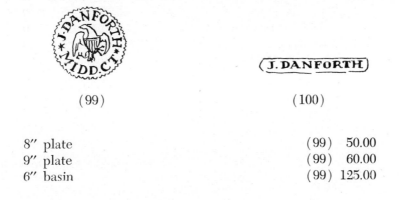

(99)   (100)

8″ plate	(99) 50.00
9″ plate	(99) 60.00
6″ basin	(99) 125.00

Fig. 9: The crown-handle porringer on the left is by John Danforth of Norwich, Conn. The same mold was used by his son, Samuel Danforth, also of Norwich. On right is a porringer cast from the same mold by Josiah Danforth of Middletown, Conn., the great-nephew of John, working 1825-1837.

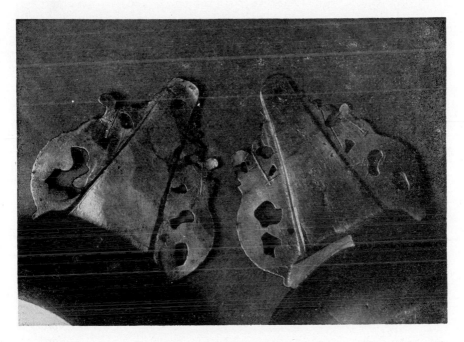

Fig. 10: Rear view of handles of Danforth porringers shown in Figure 9, with unusual spline supports.

8″ basin	(99)	65.00
*5″ range porringer,		
Old English, crown and flowered handles	(99)	175.00
*Ladle	(100)	65.00
*Teapot	(100)	35.00
Coffee pot	(100)	45.00
*Teapot, late pear-shaped	(99)	150.00
*Cuspidor	(100)	35.00
*Pint mug	(99)	200.00
*Quart mug	(99)	225.00
Ink well	(100)	150.00

DANFORTH, SAMUEL, Norwich, Connecticut, 1793-1803. Very rare.

(101)   (102)

7⅝″ plate	(101) 250.00	(102) 175.00
8⁵⁄₁₆″ plate	(101) 275.00	(102) 250.00
*12³⁄₁₆″ platter	(102) 300.00	
13⅛″ deep dish	(102) 325.00	
*5″ porringer, crown handle	(101) 500.00	

DANFORTH, SAMUEL, Hartford, Connecticut, 1795-1816. Plentiful. This very successful pewterer used more different touches than any one man in the trade. The following touches deserve premiums over the prices listed below: 103—40%, 106—15%, 107—20%, 109—20%.

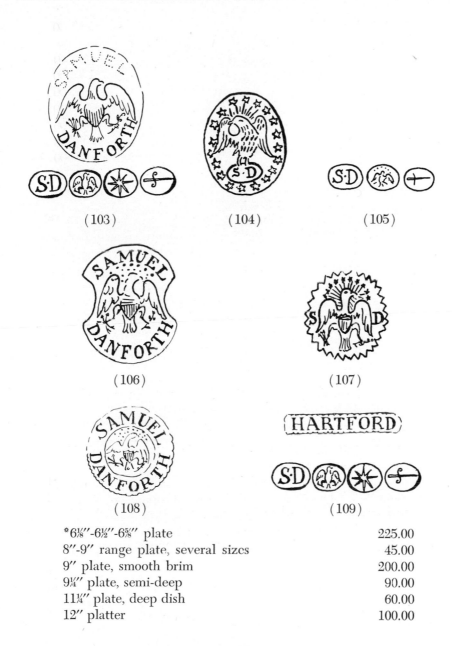

(103)   (104)   (105)

(106)   (107)

(108)   (109)

*6⅛″-6½″-6⅝″ plate   225.00
8″-9″ range plate, several sizes   45.00
9″ plate, smooth brim   200.00
9¼″ plate, semi-deep   90.00
11¼″ plate, deep dish   60.00
12″ platter   100.00

13$\frac{3}{16}$" deep dish	125.00
*4$\frac{5}{8}$" basin, very rare size	300.00
6$\frac{1}{4}$-6$\frac{5}{8}$" basin	150.00
*7$\frac{1}{4}$" basin, rare size	150.00
8" basin	60.00
10$\frac{1}{2}$" basin	95.00
Miniature mug	300.00
$\frac{1}{2}$-pint mug	250.00
Pint mug	225.00
Quart mug	250.00
Quart tankard	1500.00
Flagon, 14" tall, tiered finial, flared base	1000.00
3" beaker	175.00
5" beaker	225.00
Baptismal bowl, two types	350.00
Teapot, pear-shaped type	350.00
Teapot, same, with long base extension	350.00
3$\frac{5}{8}$"-3$\frac{3}{4}$"-4$\frac{1}{4}$"-4$\frac{3}{4}$"-5"	
Porringer, Old English handles	175.00 — 225.00
*5$\frac{1}{2}$" basin porringer, dolphin handle	350.00
*Balustre measure	800.00

Some of Samuel Danforth's distinctive forms, notably mugs from same molds as marked ones, often occur unmarked. They are well worth collecting, at about one third of the price of marked ones.

DANFORTH I, THOMAS, Taunton, Massachusetts, 1727-1733; Norwich, Connecticut, 1733-1773. If marked examples of this man's work survive, they are those bearing the "T&I" and "TD" in oval touches which have been previously assigned with considerable justification to the other partnership of Thomas II and his son, Joseph, of Middletown. The existence of plates with this mark, plus the "Norwich" scroll, makes one assign the mark to Thomas I and his son, John, but leaves the riddle of the

Fig. 11: Rare Connecticut quart tankard by Samuel Danforth of Hartford.

Fig. 12: Mark on Samuel Danforth tankard.

Fig. 13: Three plates and a range of mugs from ⅛-pint to one quart, by Samuel Danforth and the Boardmans.

Fig. 15: Rampant-lion touch probably used by Thomas Danforth 1 and his son, John Danforth.

Fig. 14: Rampant-lion touch probably used by Thomas Danforth I.

accompanying Middletown Danforth hallmarks still unsolved. The technical construction of the 9½" plate below could easily be the work of the first Thomas. *See* Appendix.

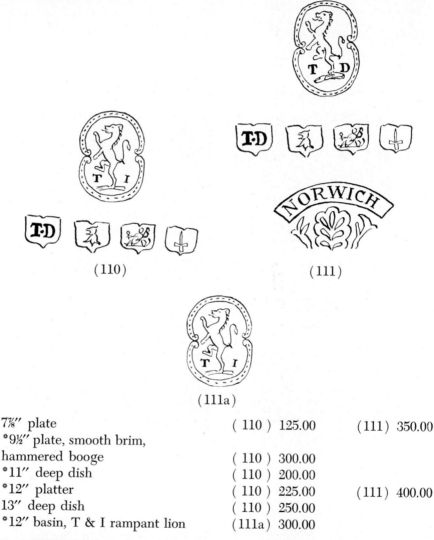

(110)   (111)

(111a)

7⅞" plate	(110)	125.00	(111) 350.00
*9½" plate, smooth brim,			
hammered booge	(110)	300.00	
*11" deep dish	(110)	200.00	
*12" platter	(110)	225.00	(111) 400.00
13" deep dish	(110)	250.00	
*12" basin, T & I rampant lion	(111a)	300.00	

DANFORTH II, THOMAS, Middletown, Connecticut, 1775-1782. Plentiful. The earliest Connecticut pewterer whose product can be definitely identified. During the war of Independence, he was commissioned to provide lead for bullets of the Continental Army. Practically all of his pewter is pre-revolutionary. The dearth of pre-revolutionary pewter at-

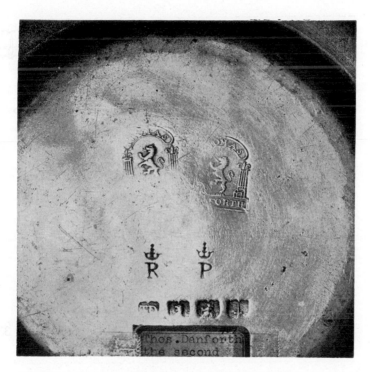

*Fig. 16: The normal touches of Thomas Danforth II, working
1755-1782, Middletown, Conn.*

Fig. 17: Porringer with Old English handle by Thomas Dan-forth II or Thomas Danforth III, 1780.

tributable to most American makers, and the rare incidence of his plates with hammered booges, would seem to indicate that much of the pewter with his touches was made by one or more of his sons. *See* JOSEPH DANFORTH, or THOMAS DANFORTH III.

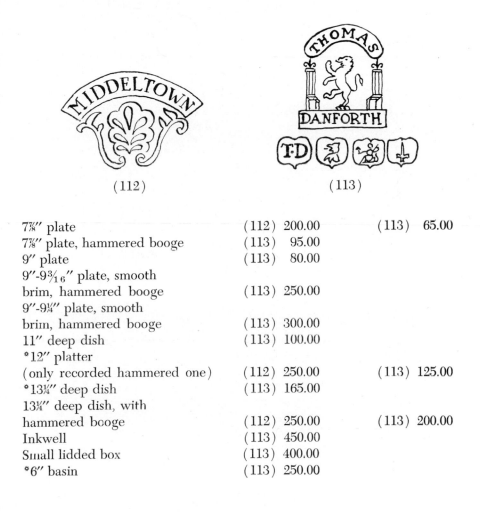

(112)   (113)

7⅞″ plate	(112) 200.00	(113) 65.00
7⅞″ plate, hammered booge	(113) 95.00	
9″ plate	(113) 80.00	
9″-9³⁄₁₆″ plate, smooth brim, hammered booge	(113) 250.00	
9″-9¼″ plate, smooth brim, hammered booge	(113) 300.00	
11″ deep dish	(113) 100.00	
*12″ platter (only recorded hammered one)	(112) 250.00	(113) 125.00
*13¼″ deep dish	(113) 165.00	
13¼″ deep dish, with hammered booge	(112) 250.00	(113) 200.00
Inkwell	(113) 450.00	
Small lidded box	(113) 400.00	
*6″ basin	(113) 250.00	

DANFORTH III, THOMAS, Stepney (Rocky Hill), Connecticut, and
Philadelphia, 1777-1818. Plentiful in Philadelphia flatware; rarer in early
Connecticut items.

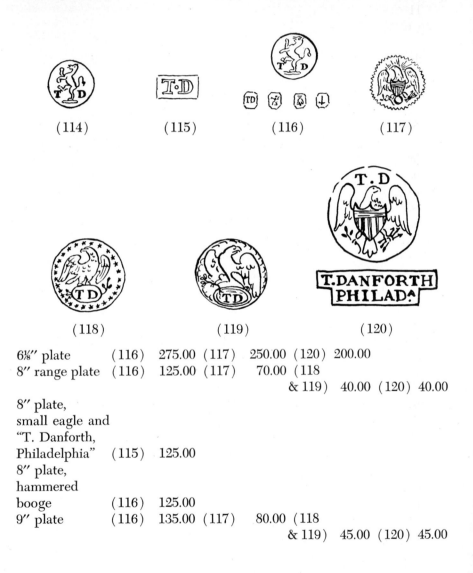

(114)   (115)   (116)   (117)

(118)   (119)   (120)

6⅛″ plate   (116) 275.00 (117) 250.00 (120) 200.00
8″ range plate (116) 125.00 (117)   70.00 (118
                                             & 119) 40.00 (120) 40.00

8″ plate,
small eagle and
"T. Danforth,
Philadelphia"   (115) 125.00
8″ plate,
hammered
booge   (116) 125.00
9″ plate   (116) 135.00 (117)   80.00 (118
                                             & 119) 45.00 (120) 45.00

9¼" plate,
smooth brim   (116)   250.00 (118
                                & 119)   225.00 (120) 225.00

11"-11⁹⁄₁₆"
deep dish   (118
               & 119)   100.00 (120)   100.00
13" deep dish (116)   200.00 (118
                                & 119)   115.00 (120) 115.00
8" basin   (116)   125.00 (118
                                & 119)   65.00 (120)   65.00
9" basin   (118
               & 119)   75.00 (120)   75.00
10" basin   (120)   110.00
12" basin   (120)   175.00
*Teapot,
pear-shaped   (115)   400.00 (116)   400.00 (120) 450.00
5" beaker   (115)   125.00 (116)   125.00
Small covered
sugar   (116)   400.00
Sugar shaker   (118   225.00
               & 119)
Pint mug   (115)   250.00 (116)   250.00
Quart mug   (115)   275.00 (116)   275.00
*Pint tankard (114)   1500.00
Quart tankard (115)   1500.00 (116) 1500.00
3⅜"-4" range
porringer, Old
English handles (116)   400.00
5⅜" porringer,
solid handle   (118   450.00
               & 119)
*5" porringer
flowered
handle   (116)   325.00 (117)   450.00 (118   450.00
                                                 & 119)
*Pint tankard (121)   1500.00

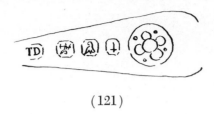

(121)

*Tablespoon,
flower mark
with hallmarks (121)   400.00

This spoon, dug up on the site of the famed seventeenth-century Buttolph-Williams house, in Wethersfield, Connecticut, now property of the Connecticut Antiquarium Society, is the key that ties in the no name "rose" touch with the Stepney, Connecticut, hallmarks of Thomas Danforth III. A rare, early, and important spoon.

DANFORTH IV, THOMAS, Philadelphia, and Augusta, Georgia, 1792-1836.
     This man worked for other pewterers. He may have been an independent worker at some time during his life.
No known examples.

DANFORTH, WILLIAM, Middletown, Connecticut, 1792-1820. Scarce. Though one of the last of the Danforths, his pewter is uncommon.

(122)

(123)

7⅞″ plate   (122)   65.00   (123)   60.00
8¾″ plate   (123)   65.00

Fig. 18: The tankard on the left is by Benjamin Day; the one on the right, though unmarked, may well be "RB" of Newport or Boston. A smooth-brim plate (second from left) is by Thomas Byles of Newport, Camden, and Philadelphia.

11¼″ deep dish   (123)   95.00
13³⁄₁₆″ deep dish   (123)   125.00
8″ basin   (122)   85.00

*DAVIS, EDMUND, Philadelphia, Pennsylvania, 1721-17—.
No known examples.

DAY, BENJAMIN, Newport, Rhode Island, 1706-1757. Extremely rare.

(124)

5″ porringer, solid handle   750.00
Quart mug, squat; actually a lidless tankard   950.00
Quart tankard with finial, hammered all
over; unique in American pewter   2500.00

DERBY, THOMAS S., Middletown, Connecticut, 1812-1852. Scarce in
pewter. In his early years, this man made pewter. Later on he made
britannia, which is of poor form and workmanship, and of little interest.
His pewter, especially that with the historic General Jackson touch, is
of great interest to collectors. Later forms were also made in partnership with his son, Thomas S. Derby, Jr., and by the latter alone.

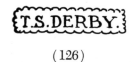

(125)   (126)

8″-8¾″ plate	(125) 250.00	(126) 125.00
13¼″ deep dish	(125) 450.00	
6″ basin	(125) 350.00	(126) 175.00
11½″ basin	(125) 375.00	
Teapot	(126) 45.00	
Coffee pot	(126) 60.00	
Cuspidor	(126) 45.00	

DE RIEMER, CORNELIUS B. & CO., Auburn, New York, 1835.
Britannia. Scarce.

3″ beaker	65.00

*DIETZ BROS. & CO., location unknown, possibly New York City or Cincinnati, Ohio. Late. This company made cigar lighters and perhaps other forms.

DIGGS, WILLIAM, New York City, 1702.
No known examples.

DOLBEARE, EDMUND, Boston, 1671-1702.
*A few multiple reeded platters with "ID" and "ED" touches occur. These are unlisted in the English books, and have been accepted as American by leading authorities.

(127)

*13⅛″-15″- 15⁵⁄₁₆ platter	750.00

Fig. 19: A quart basin and a small plate, both bearing the marks of John Dolbeare of Devonshire, England, and Boston. Both pieces show evidence of American manufacture.

DOLBEARE, JOHN, Boston, 1690-1740.
See DOLBEARE, EDMUND, above.

(128)

(129)

9¼″ plate	(129)	1800.00
8″ basin	(129)	2000.00
*13⅛″-15¹⁵⁄₁₆″ platter	(128)	750.00

DOLBEARE, JOSEPH, Boston, 1690-1704.
No known examples.

DOLBEARE and JACKSON (John Dolbeare and Jonathan Jackson)
Boston, 1725. No known examples of this partnership.

DOUGHERTY, Newark, New Jersey, 1845.
See BROWE and DOUGHERTY.

DUNHAM, E., Maine, 1830's. Rare. Britannia.
    Lamp, single   35.00

DUNHAM, RUFUS, Westbrook, Maine, 1837-1861. Plentiful. Britannia.
Also DUNHAM, R., and SONS, Portland, Maine, 1861-1882.

Lamp, as to size and form	single,	15.00—25.00;	pair,	45.00—75.00
6″ candlestick	single,	20.00;	pair,	50.00
6″ candlestick, with saucer base	single,	45.00;	pair,	125.00
2-quart pitcher	open,	45.00;	lidded,	75.00
Teapot, various styles		20.00—35.00		
Coffee pot, various styles		25.00—45.00		
Flagon		65.00		

*China tea tile,
pewter cased and footed;
unique in American pewter,
6" x 6¼", rare   125.00
*3½" beaker   40.00

*DUNLOP, H. & CO., Philadelphia, Pa. 1830. Britannia. Rare.

    *10" plate, unique   95.00

DURNINGER, DANIEL, Boston, 1722-1723.
No known examples.

EADEM, SEMPER
See SEMPER EADEM; SKINNER, JOHN; and B., R.

EDGELL, SIMON, Philadelphia, 1713-1742. Extremely rare. This man
was a master pewterer, and one of the earliest American workers whose
products have been found. There are perhaps ten examples extant. His
flatware, hammered all over, is almost unique in American pewter.

        (130)   (131)

    9¼" plate, smooth brim, hammered booge   600.00
    *Hot water plate   1500.00
    15" platter, deep, hammered all over   2000.00
    16⅜ platter, deep, hammered all over   3000.00
    *19" charger, largest known in American pewter 5000.00
    Quart tankard   3000.00

EDGELL, WILLIAM, Boston, 1724.
No known examples.

EGGLESTON, JACOB, Middletown, Connecticut, 1795-1807; Fayetteville, North Carolina, 1807-1813. Rare. Eggleston was one of the several

Fig. 20: Seventeenth-century platter with multiple reed rim attributed to John Dolbeare of Boston; "ID" initials in heart-shaped outline, repeated four times.

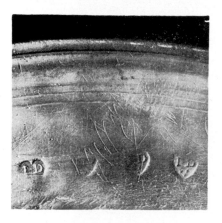

Fig. 21: Marks on a seventeenth-century multiple reed rim platter, attributed to John Dolbeare.

Fig. 22: The mark of John Dolbeare, Sr., used in England, here on a plate of characteristic Boston construction, probably made in America by a descendant.

Connecticut Valley pewterers who, under the stress of competition, migrated to the south. The initial touch appears to be the later one and was probably used in Fayetteville.

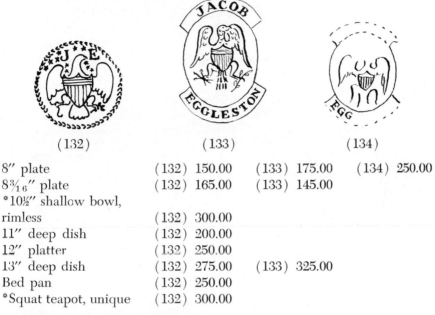

(132) (133) (134)

8" plate	(132) 150.00	(133) 175.00	(134) 250.00
8³⁄₁₆" plate	(132) 165.00	(133) 145.00	
*10½" shallow bowl, rimless	(132) 300.00		
11" deep dish	(132) 200.00		
12" platter	(132) 250.00		
13" deep dish	(132) 275.00	(133) 325.00	
Bed pan	(132) 250.00		
*Squat teapot, unique	(132) 300.00		

ELDRIGE, ELI, Boston, 1849; Taunton, Massachusetts, 1860. No known examples.

ELLISON, JOHN, Philadelphia, Pa., 1837. No known examples.

ELLSWORTH, WILLIAM J., New York City, 1767-1798. Very rare.

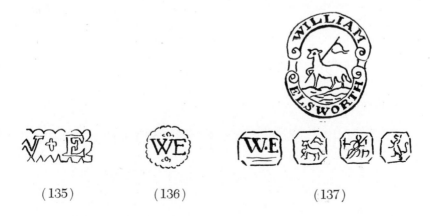

(135) (136) (137)

(138)

7⅞″-8¼″ plates	(137)	400.00
9″ plate	(137)	425.00
*11¾″ platter	(137)	500.00
13¼″ platter	(138)	600.00
15″ platter	(138)	750.00
8″ basin	(135)	400.00

Quart tankard, two types,
one low double dome top,
one flat top   (136) 2500.00   (138) 2500.00
*Slip top spoon   (138) 400.00

ENDICOTT, EDMUND, New York City, 1846-1853. Scarce. Britannia.

    Lamp   Swivel 45.00   Others 25.00

ENDICOTT and SUMNER (Edmund Endicott and William F. Sumner),
New York City, 1846-1851. Plentiful. Britannia.
    Lamp   Swivel 45.00   Others 25.00
    Candlesticks, as to
    size,   pair 50.00—75.00

*ENGEL, GEORGE, Philadelphia, Pa., 1850.
No known examples.

ENGLAND, N. ("N. England" in rectangle). See MELVILLE, DAVID.

ESTABROOK, RICHARD, Boston, Massachusetts, 1720.
No known examples.

EVERETT, JAMES, Philadelphia, Pa., 1716.
No known American examples. The clasped hand and initial touch used by him in England is illustrated in H. H. Cotterell's, *Old Pewter—Its Makers and Their Marks* (No. 1597).

FELTMAN, JAMES, Albany, New York, 1847-1848.
See SHELDON and FELTMAN.

FENN, GAIUS and JASON, New York City, 1831-1843. Scarce.

Inkwell (marked American inkwells are rare)	100.00
Molasses gate, unique	75.00
Faucet, various types	45.00
*Ladle	65.00

FIELDS, PHILIP, New York City, 1799.
No known examples.

*FISCHER, JOHN, Pennsylvania, late eighteenth century. Very rare.
Also FISCHER, I. & T. The first mark is of doubtful attribution.

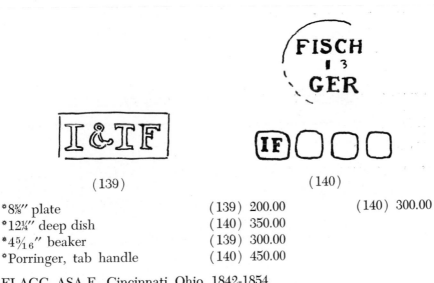

(139)   (140)

*8⅝″ plate	(139) 200.00	(140) 300.00
*12¼″ deep dish	(140) 350.00	
*4⁵⁄₁₆″ beaker	(139) 300.00	
*Porringer, tab handle	(140) 450.00	

FLAGG, ASA F., Cincinnati, Ohio, 1842-1854.
See FLAGG and HOMAN.

FLAGG, DAVID, Boston, Massachusetts, 1750-1772.
No known examples.

FLAGG and HOMAN (Asa F. Flagg and Henry Homan), Cincinnati, Ohio, 1842-1854. Plentiful.

Teapot	25.00—45.00
Syrup pitcher, late form	35.00
Candlesticks, pair	65.00
Lamps, pair	75.00
Pint mug, late style	45.00
*3″ beaker (HOMAN & CO.)	35.00
*Wine goblet, unique in American pewter	45.00
Grease lamp, earlier Continental type, unique with American mark (HOMAN & CO.)	150.00
*4¼″ porringer, keyhole handle, hammered boss, late, but unique	100.00
*4¼″ porringer, not hammered	75.00
*Footed sauce boat	85.00

FLETCHER, THOMAS, Philadelphia, 1837-1841.
No known examples.

FRANCIS, DANIEL, Buffalo, New York, 1833-1842.
See WHITMORE and FRANCIS.

FRANCIS, THOMAS, Boston, 1718.
No known examples.

FRARY, JAMES A., Meriden, Connecticut, 1845-1849. Britannia. Also FRARY and BENHAM (James A. Frary and Morris Benham), Meriden, Connecticut, 1849.
No known examples.

*FRINK, NATHANIEL, Northampton, Massachusetts, 1820.

(141)

*8" basin, unique   250.00

FRYERS, JOHN, Newport, Rhode Island, c. 1705-1776. Extremely rare.

(142)

*Pint lidded "bud" thumbpiece
balustre measure   1500.00
Quart mug   950.00
*Quart tankard, finial on cover   2000.00
*Commode form, 9¼" tall, mark
on outside base   600.00

FULLER and SMITH, Poquonock Bridge (New London), Connecticut 1850. Scarce.

Lamps, pair   75.00
Candlesticks, pair   65.00

—Y and GARDNER, Location unknown, 1840. Scarce.

Teapot   30.00

*G., H., Probably Boston, Massachusetts; possibly Henry Green.

(143)

*8⁹⁄₁₆" shallow plate   250.00

G., I., Probably Virginia, mid-18th century. Extremely rare.

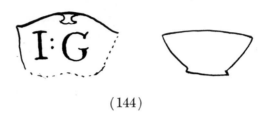

(144)

    *8⅞″ plate, smooth brim, marked under brim   300.00

G., I., New England, 1800. Touch cast on under side of porringer handles.

    4″ range porringer, crown handle   35.00

G., R., New England, early nineteenth century. Possibly Roswell Gleason. Scarce. Touch cast on under side of porringer handles.

    4″ range porringer, crown handle   45.00

G., S., (S reversed), New England, 1800. Touch cast at end of under side of handle.

    4″ range porringer, crown handle   35.00
    5″ range porringer, crown handle   40.00

GEANTY, LEWIS, Baltimore, Maryland, 1800-1803.
No known examples.

GEORGE, ANTHONY, JR., Philadelphia, Pa., 1839-1847.
No known examples.

GERHARDT & CO., location unknown, 1840. Scarce. Britannia.

    Snuff box (a rare form in marked American pewter)   65.00
    *Sugar bowl   35.00
    *Creamer   35.00
    *Teapot   35.00

GLEASON, ROSWELL, Dorchester, Massachusetts, 1822-1871. Plentiful. He was a superior craftsman, working in both pewter and britannia, and enjoyed a very large trade. His design and quality were better than those of most of his contemporaries. The eagle touch is his earliest and is worth a twenty percent premium. His Massachusetts coat of arms touch is very rare and deserves at least a one-hundred percent premium. The small, full name touch on the porringer listed below is unique, and perhaps his earliest mark.

(145)   (146)   (147)

ROSWELL GLEASON   ROSWELL GLEASON

(148)   (149)

8″ plate, eagle touch	60.00
9″-11″ plate, later, for Communion	20.00
Cuspidor	30.00
*Wash basin with handle, large, rare form	125.00
Teapot, ordinary form, as to size	25.00—35.00
*Teapot, late pear-shaped, with small base extension	150.00
Teapot, globe-shaped	50.00
Teapot, pigeon-breasted	45.00
Lighthouse coffee pot	40.00
Coffee pot, pigeon-breasted	60.00
Flagon	65.00
Chalices, pair	75.00
Baptismal bowl	125.00
Coffee urn	125.00
3″ beaker	45.00
Covered syrup pitcher	60.00

Cruet set	25.00
Ladle	65.00
2-quart covered pitcher	75.00
Gallon covered water pitcher	150.00
Candlesticks, pair	75.00
Lamps, pair, as to style and size	40.00—125.00
Lamp, bulls-eye lens (only known marked American examples)	100.00
*3″-4″ range porringer, heart handle, RG cast under handle	75.00
*3″-4″ range porringer, with only "R" showing	35.00
2⅝″ porringer, perforated handle, rectangle name touch under handle, unique	200.00
*Pint mug, early form	175.00
Pint mug, later style, broken C handle	45.00
*1½ pint mug	60.00
Quart tankard, screw top, unique form	250.00
*Bed pan	75.00
*Cigar lighter	75.00
Shaving mug, unique	250.00

GLENNORE COMPANY, Cranston, Rhode Island, after 1825.
(*See* RICHARDSON, G.)

*GOOCH, JOHN, Locale unknown. Before 1750.
No known examples.

GRAHAM, JOHN B. and JASPER, Middletown, Connecticut, after 1835.
See SAVAGE, WILLIAM.

GRAME, SAMUEL, Boston, Massachusetts, 1639-1645.
No known examples.

GRAVES, JOSHUA B., and HENRY H., Middletown, Connecticut, 1850.
Plentiful. Britannia.

Teapot	25.00
Candlestick, as to size	45.00—65.00

GREAVES, RICHARD, Salem, Massachusetts, 1635-1667.
No known examples.

GREEN, ANDREW, Boston, Massachusetts, 1773-1798.
No known examples.

GREEN, JONAS, Boston, Massachusetts, 1786-1787.
No known examples. Possibly the maker of the "I G" porringers.

GREEN, SAMUEL, Boston, Massachusetts, 1794-1830. From 1814-1816, he was a partner with Richard Austin. In 1818 he was a partner with George Richardson. No touch attributable to either partnership has been found. Green used two scroll name touches, which are of equal value. His eight-inch plates are much rarer than his larger ones.

(150)   (151)

4⅞" plate, smallest known in American pewter	500.00
*6" plate	400.00
8" plate, three sizes	200.00
*9" plate	250.00
12³⁄₁₆" deep dish	175.00
13" platter	175.00
13½" platter	175.00
6" basin	275.00
8" basin	225.00

Boston basins are indeed rare.

GREEN, SAMUEL, JR., Boston, Massachusetts, 1821-1835.
No known examples. Possibly the maker of the numerous "S G" crown handled porringers.

GREEN, THOMAS, Boston, Massachusetts, 1715-1794. Though he was the senior member of the numerous pewtering Greens of New London and Boston, and enjoyed a large trade, no pieces attributable to him have been found.

GREEN, THOMAS, JR., Boston, Massachusetts, 1769-1786.
No known examples.

Fig. 23: New England tankards by Benjamin Day, Samuel Danforth, and "IC" or "IG," early eighteenth-century Boston or New London. The latter perhaps by one of the Greens.

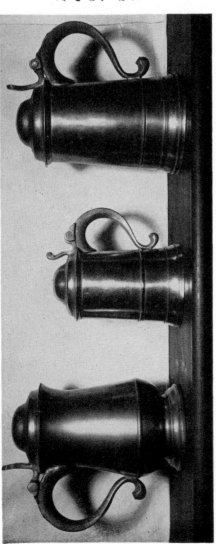

Fig. 24: Pennsylvania pewter. Notable on the top shelf are the very similar quart tankards by "Love" and Parks Boyd, the rare little pint tankard by Cornelius Bradford, and the solid handle porringer by Robert Porter; on the bottom shelf, a smooth-brim Brunstrom plate and a barrel-shaped pint mug by Palethorpe.

GREEN, TIMOTHY, Boston, Massachusetts, 1780-1782. Also reported
to have worked in New London, Connecticut.
No known examples.

GRINDELL (GRENNELL), THOMAS, New York City, 1790.
No known examples.

GRISWOLD, ASHBIL, Meriden, Connecticut, *1802-1842. He worked
in both pewter and britannia, and his products are plentiful.

(152)

(153)

(154)

(155)

8″ plate	(152)	45.00	(153)	37.50
8½″ plate	(152)	47.50	(153)	40.00
11″ deep dish	(152)	75.00		
13″ deep dish	(152)	100.00	(153)	90.00
13″ deep dish, with General Jackson				
touch (See also DERBY, THOMAS, S.)	(152)	300.00		

8″ basin	(152)	65.00	(153)	60.00
9″ basin	(152)	80.00	(153)	75.00
10¼″ basin	(152)	100.00		
12″ basin	(152)	175.00		
Teapot	(154)	35.00		
Teapot, pear-shaped	(153)	165.00	(154)	150.00
Coffee pot	(154)	45.00		
3″ beaker	(155)	40.00		
Inkwell, small covered box, shaving dish	(155)	125.00		
Inkwell, small covered box, shaving dish, unmarked		40.00		
Ladle	(155)	65.00		
Sugar bowl	(154)	35.00		

*5⅚₁₆″ porringer, geometric, with heart aperture. Touch on back of handle. Very rare. (153) 250.00

GRISWOLD, GILES, Augusta, Georgia, 1820. Extremely rare.

(156)

*8″ plate   450.00

GRISWOLD, SYLVESTER, Baltimore, Maryland, 1820. Rare.

(157)

7¾″ plate	250.00
13″ deep dish	300.00
8″ basin	275.00

GRISWOLD and COUCH, Meriden, Connecticut, 1830.
No examples of this partnership, Ashbil Griswold and Ira Couch, are known.

*H., G., (Shield with "GH-NY"). New York City, 1840's. Rare. Britannia.

    *5-pint coffee pot   95.00

*H., D. M., (DMH in rectangle), Meriden, Connecticut, 1830's. Scarce.

    *Teapot   75.00

HALL, FRANKLIN D.
See HALL, BOARDMAN, and COMPANY under BOARDMAN, THOMAS DANFORTH.

HALL, JOHN H.
See JOHNSON, JEHIEL.

HALL, BOARDMAN and CO., Philadelphia, 1840's. This is a late firm name for the Philadelphia outlet of Thomas Danforth Boardman and partners.

HALL and COTTON, *Middlefield, Connecticut, 1840's.
Scarce. Britannia.

Covered syrup pitcher	45.00
Inkwell	125.00
*Ladle	65.00
*Sander	125.00
*Pint mug, with double C handle	60.00
*Pint teapot	85.00

*HALL, ELTON & CO., Wallingford, Connecticut, 1860. Britannia.
No known examples.

HAMLIN, SAMUEL, *1767-1801; Hartford, Connecticut, and Providence,
Rhode Island. HAMLIN, SAMUEL E., JR., Providence, Rhode Island,
1801-1856. Plentiful, though rather uncommon in flatware. Their porringers are found more often than those of any other maker, with the
possible exception of the Boardmans. Some of the touches were used by
both men.

*Before moving to Providence, Samuel Hamlin was a member of the
firm of HENSHAW and HAMLIN in Hartford from 1767 to 1769. They
were braziers and pewterers at the shop of Window Hooker, near the
North Meeting house. Benjamin Henshaw was the elder of the two
men and may have invested money in the enterprise without being a
pewterer as such.

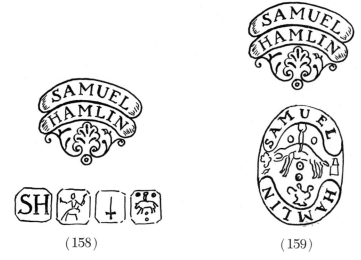

(158)   (159)

These touches used by both Hamlins.

(160)   (161)   (162)

These touches used only by Hamlin, Sr.

8¼″ plate	(158) 95.00	(159) 150.00
9¼″ plate	(158) 110.00	(159) 175.00
9⅛″ plate, smooth brim	(158) 250.00	(159) 300.00
11½″ dish, deep	(158) 75.00	
13″ dish	(158) 100.00	
13¼″ dish	(158) 100.00	
13½″ dish	(158) 100.00	
14″ dish (rare size in American pewter)	(158) 150.00	
14¾″ dish	(158) 150.00	
15″ dish	(158) 150.00	
Miniature basin, 3⅝″—2¹³/₁₆″	(162) 350.00	
Basin, 5¾″—2¹³/₁₆″	(158) 125.00	(162) 150.00
Basin, 7¾″—8″	(158) 75.00	
Basin, 10½″	(158) 95.00	
*3″ beaker	(162) 150.00	
*¼ pint mug, double C handle, with variant no-name "rose" touch	(160) 350.00	
Pint mug, double C handle	(158) 225.00	
Quart mug	(158) 250.00	
4³/₁₆″ porringer, flowered handle	(161) 125.00	(162) 115.00
4⅜″—4⅝″ porringer, Old English handle	(161) 125.00	(162) 115.00
5¼″ porringer, flowered handle	(160) 350.00	(161) 125.00 (162) 115.00

HAMLIN, SAMUEL E., JR., Providence, Rhode Island, 1801-1856. Plentiful. Touches below were used only by Hamlin, Jr.

(163)   (164)   (165)

3″ beaker   (165)   75.00
*Ladle   (165) 110.00
4³⁄₁₆″ porringer, flowered handle   (163) 115.00
4⅜″—4⅝″ porringer, flowered handle   (163) 115.00   (164) 250.00
4⅜″—4⅝″ porringer, Old English handle   (163) 115.00
5¼″—5½″ porringer, flowered handle   (163) 115.00   (164) 250.00

HAMLIN and JONES, Providence, Rhode Island, 1774-1781.
No known examples of this partnership, though the pear-shaped teapot illustrated with the wooden handle and the "H.J" mark may tentatively be attributed to the firm.

HARBESON, BENJAMIN and JOSEPH, Philadelphia, 1765-1775, 1778-1800; *Lancaster, Pennsylvania, 1775-1778. In 1793, Joseph and Benjamin, Jr., sons, joined the enterprise. Later the sons relocated in Germantown, now a part of Philadelphia. Though early and scarce, their pewter is often very leady and poorly finished.

(166)

5⅞″ plate   250.00
7⅞″ plate   65.00
8¾″ plate   70.00
11″ deep dish   100.00
13⅛″ deep dish   150.00
6⅝″ basin   175.00
10¼″ basin   135.00

HARNER, GEORGE, New York City, 1760.
No known examples.

HARRISON, JOSEPH, Philadelphia, 1829-1852.
No known examples.

HART, LUCIUS D.
See BOARDMAN, THOMAS DANFORTH.

HASSELBERG, ABRAHAM, Philadelphia, 1762-1769. *1759, Wilmington, Delaware. He was related to Brunstrom and to Kehler.
No known examples.

HENDRICKS, FRANCIS G., Charlestown, South Carolina, 1771-1784.
No known examples.

HENRY, ANDREW, Orange County, New York, 1761.
No known examples.

*HENSHAW, BENJAMIN, Hartford and Middletown, Connecticut, b. 1731; d. 1793. (*See* HAMLIN, SAMUEL).
No known examples.

*HENSHAW and HAMLIN (Benjamin Henshaw and Samuel Hamlin), Hart, Connecticut, 1767. (*See* HAMLIN, SAMUEL).
No known examples.

HERA, CHRISTIAN, Philadelphia, 1791-1817.
No known examples.

HERA, C. and J. (Christian and John Hera), Philadelphia, 1800-1812.
Extremely rare.

(167)

9¼″ smooth brim plate   500.00

Fig. 25: The early pear-shaped teapot in the center has the "H.J." mark which may be the missing touch of the partnership of Hamlin and Jones. The transitional pear-shaped teapots flanking it were made in the same mold by Samuel Danforth and Thomas D. Boardman

Fig. 26: Combination touch on teapot attributed to the partnership of Hamlin and Jones of Providence. The teapot is illustrated in Figure 25.

HERA, JOHN, Philadelphia, 1800-1812.
No known examples.

HERA II, JOHN, Philadelphia, 1817-1821.
No known examples.

HERSEY, S. S., *Belfast, Maine, 1830's. He was the northernmost pewterer in the country whose work still survives. Britannia.

Teapot, truncated lighthouse, two types	40.00
*Communion flagon	60.00
*3″ beaker	45.00

HEYNE, JOHANN CHRISTOPHER, Lancaster, Pennsylvania, 1754-1780. Extremely rare. Heyne's hollow-ware, combining Germanic and English designs, is among the most distinctive of American pewter. In addition to uniqueness of design, his chalices and flagons are the earliest found in marked American pewter.

(168)

(169)

6″ plate	600.00
*6½″ plate	600.00
7⅞″ plate	400.00
*Beaker	850.00
Dram bottle	1200.00
Sugar bowl	1000.00
8¾″ open chalice	marked, 950.00; unmarked 475.00
8¾″ covered chalice (two forms)	marked, 1500.00; unmarked 750.00
Communion flagon, (two forms)	3500.00
Porringer, Old English handle	1000.00
*Open salt, 3¼″ high	800.00

Fig. 27: A varied group of chalices and beakers, mostly unmarked. Many attributable to known makers by comparison with identical marked pieces. Top row: chalice, I. Trask; beaker, Massachusetts, about 1800; chalice, Lancaster, Pa., eighteenth century, probably by Heyne; beaker, 1760, John Bassett; chalice, Pennsylvania, eighteenth century; beaker, Pennsylvania, mid-eighteenth century, marked "I & TF"; chalice, nineteenth century, I. Trask (note foot made from flagon-cover mold); beaker, Massachusetts, about 1800. Bottom row: Church cup, Boston or New York, early eighteenth century (a great rarity and valuable though unmarked); beaker, Greenfield, Mass., about 1800, Samuel Pierce mold; chalice with cup made from preceding beaker-mold; beaker, probably Danforth or Boardman; chalice, Boardman; beaker, Hartford, about 1800, Danforth or Boardman; chalice, about 1840, Leonard, Reed, and Barton; beaker, New England, early nineteenth century; small beaker, Connecticut or Massachusetts, about 1820. (All from the collection of John F. Ruckman.)

HILL, JOHN, New York City, 1840's. Britannia.
No known examples.

HILLSBURGH, CHARLES, New York City, 1830's. Britannia.
No known examples.

HINSDALE, J. and D. (John and Daniel Hinsdale), Middletown, Connecticut, 1815. Extremely rare.

(170)

8¾″ plate	250.00
8″ basin	275.00

HOLMES, ROBERT and SONS, Baltimore, Maryland, 1850's. Britannia.
Scarce.

Tea and coffee pots, late, poor design	15.00—20.00
Lamps, pair	50.00

HOLT, THOMAS R., Meriden, Connecticut, 1845-1849. Britannia. Scarce.

Spoon	8.00

HOLYOKE, JOHN, Boston, 1683-1775.
No known examples.

HOMAN, HENRY: HOMAN & CO.: HOMAN & FLAGG.
See FLAGG and HOMAN.

*HOOKER, "THE WIDOW," Hartford, Connecticut, 1767. (See HAM-
LIN, SAMUEL). Perhaps she was the wife of a pewterer or a brazier.

HOPPER, HENRY, New York City, 1842-1847. Britannia. His products
were superior in design and finish.

Lamps, pair, as to style and size	70.00—100.00
9″ candlesticks, plain, pair	60.00
10″ candlesticks, engraved, pair	90.00
12″ candlesticks, engraved, pair	125.00
Pint water pitcher, open, unique size	135.00
*Pint water pitcher, covered	160.00
2-quart water pitcher, open	85.00
2-quart water, pitcher, covered	100.00
Gallon water pitcher, covered	175.00
*Ladle	65.00
*Fife	125.00

HORAN, JOHANN CHRISTIAN (HERA?), Philadelphia, 1758-1786. Extremely rare. (*See* ALBERTI and HORAN.) This mark might be attributed to I. C. Heyne with equal justification.

(171)

9⁵⁄₁₆″ plate	450.00

HORSEWELL, WILLIAM, New York City, 1705-1709. The quart mug illustrated in Fig. 31 is attributed to this maker.

HORSFORD, E. N., Locale unknown, 1830's. Britannia. Rare.

Lamp	25.00

HOUGHTON and WALLACE, Philadelphia, 1840's. Rare. Britannia.

Lamp	25.00

HOUSE, EDWIN, Hartford, Connecticut, 1841-1846. Probably a Boardman worker.
No known examples.

HUMISTON, WILLIS, Troy, New York, 1840-1860. Britannia. Rare.

Teapot	25.00
Candle mold in wooden frame.	65.00

HUNT, S., locale unknown, c. 1840. Britannia. Rare.

Teapot	25.00

HUNTER, GEORGE, Troy, New York, 1831. Possibly an employee only.
No known examples.

HYDE, MARTIN, New York City, 1850's. Britannia. Scarce.

Candlesticks, pair	50.00
Swivel lamp	45.00

I, T. & *See* DANFORTH I, THOMAS.

ISLY, JOSEPH, New York City, 1715.
No known examples.

*JACKSON, ISAAC, Pennsylvania, late eighteenth century. Very rare.

*Porringer, tab handle	250.00

JAGGER, DANIEL, JAMES and WALTER, Hartford, Connecticut,
1840's. Probably employees.
No known examples.

JANNEY, N. E., St. Louis, 1846.
See ARCHER and JANNEY

JENNINGS, THEODORE, Maryland, 1775.
No known examples.

JOHNSON, JEHIEL, Middletown, Connecticut, 1815-1825. Fayetteville,
North Carolina, 1818-1819. Very Scarce. Johnson also worked in partner-
ship with Constant Johnson and John H. Hall (JOHNSON, HALL, and
CO., Middletown, Connecticut, 1815-1817), and with William Nott
(JOHNSON and NOTT, Middletown, Connecticut and Fayetteville,
North Carolina, 1817-1819).
No known touches for either partnership.

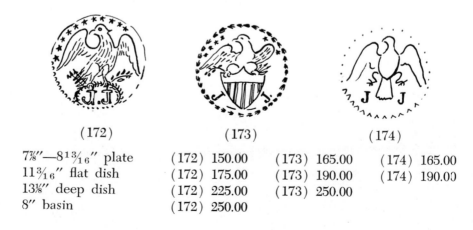

(172)   (173)   (174)

7⅞″—8¹³⁄₁₆″ plate	(172)	150.00	(173)	165.00	(174)	165.00
11³⁄₁₆″ flat dish	(172)	175.00	(173)	190.00	(174)	190.00
13⅛″ deep dish	(172)	225.00	(173)	250.00		
8″ basin	(172)	250.00				

JONES, DANIEL, Boston, 1705.
No known examples.

JONES, EDWARD, New York City, 1837-1850. Britannia. Rare.

　　Lamps, as to style and size, pair　　　　　　60.00—90.00

JONES, GERSHOM, Providence, Rhode Island, 1774-1809. Plentiful in
flatware, scarce in porringers, rare in hollow-ware. He worked in partnership with Samuel Hamlin (HAMLIN and JONES, 1774-1780), and with
his sons, James and Samuel Jones (GERSHOM JONES and SONS, 1806-
1807).
No known touch for either partnership. Plates are found with two
or three of his later touches, as well as his later hallmarks. Earlier touches
on plates are his small hallmarks and the double gateway lion marks.
Note the change from the older "I" to "J" just after the Revolution. The
plain eagle is found only on basins.

(175)

(176)

(177)

Fig. 28: Typical Rhode Island porringer with flowered handle by Gershom Jones of Providence, late eighteenth century; porringer with Old English handle by Henry Will of New York City and Albany. (Photo courtesy of Holmes I. Mettee.)

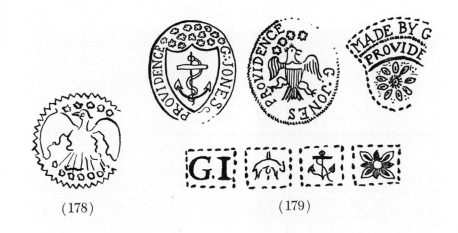

(178)   (179)

8″ plate, 3 sizes	(175) 100.00	(179) 60.00
9⅛″ plate	(175) 125.00	(179) 80.00
13½″—14½″ deep dish	(175) 225.00	(179) 175.00
14½″ deep dish	(175) 260.00	(179) 185.00
15″ deep dish, hammered booge	(175) 300.00	
*6″ basin	(178) 125.00	
8″ basin	(178) 75.00	
Quart mug, strap handle	(175) 400.00	(176) 400.00
*Quart mug, hollow handle	(176) 350.00	
4⅛″ porringer, flowered handle	(176) 300.00	(177) 200.00
5″—5⅜″—5½″ porringer, flowered handle	(176) 300.00	(177) 200.00

Note the striking resemblance to touches of John Danforth of Norwich. Perhaps the dies were from the same maker.

*K., D. H., Meriden, Connecticut, 1840. Britannia. Scarce.

    *Teapot   60.00

K., D. W. (*See* DE WITT KIMBERLY)

*KAUFFMAN, ERNEST, Philadelphia, Pa. 1850.
No known examples.

Fig. 29: Southern pewter. The plates are by Nott, Johnson, Lightner, Sylvester Griswold, and Eggleston. The superb pint mug is by Samuel Kilbourn.

Fig. 30: A range of basins: 5¾", Samuel Hamlin; 6½", William Kirby; 7¾", Gershom Jones; 8", Frederick Bassett; 9", Joseph Belcher; 9¾", John Bassett; 10¼", Jacob Whitmore; 11", Frederick Bassett; and 12", by one of the Norwich Danforths.

KEENE, JOSIAH, Providence, Rhode Island, 1801-1817. Extremely rare.

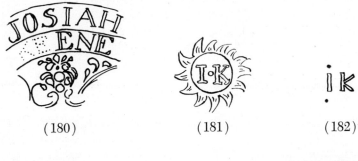

(180)   (181)   (182)

8¼″ plate	(180)	400.00
5⅜″ porringer, flowered handle	(181)	500.00
*Spoon (attribution questionable)	(182)	45.00

Known to have made 6″ plates; none extant.

KEHLER, ADAM, Philadelphia, 1780-1783. Related to Brunstrom and to Hasselberg.
No known examples.

KIERSTED, LUKE, New York City, 1805.
No known examples.

KILBOURN, SAMUEL, Baltimore, Maryland, 1814-1839. He lived in Hartford, Connecticut from 1794-1813. He worked in partnership with Jephtha Porter (KILBOURN and PORTER) in Baltimore from 1814-1816, but no known examples of this partnership have been discovered.

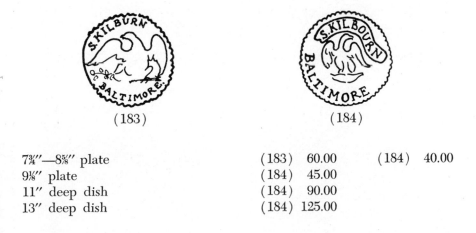

(183)   (184)

7¾″—8⅝″ plate	(183)	60.00	(184)	40.00
9⅝″ plate	(184)	45.00		
11″ deep dish	(184)	90.00		
13″ deep dish	(184)	125.00		

8″ basin	(184)	85.00
10″ basin	(184)	110.00
12″ basin	(184)	175.00
*3⅜″ beaker	(183)	125.00
Pint mug (excellent form)	(184)	225.00
Quart mug	(184)	200.00
*Bed pan	(184)	125.00
*Modified pear-shaped tea pot	(183)	350.00

Latter almost identical to Samuel Danforth's.

KIMBERLY, DE WITT, Meriden, Connecticut, 1845-1849. Britannia. Scarce.
No known examples.

KIRBY, PETER, New York City, 1736-1788. Extremely rare.

(185)

4¼″ porringer, Old English handle   850.00

KIRBY, WILLIAM, New York City, 1760-1793. Very rare.

(186)   (187)   (188)   (189)

8³⁄₁₆" plate, hammered booge	(188)	400.00
9" plate, hammered booge	(188)	450.00
4¼" porringer, Old English handle	(187)	750.00
6" basin	(189)	450.00
Quart mug, fishtail handle	(189)	700.00
Quart tankard, dome top, crenate lip, fishtail handle	(186)	2000.00
Quart tankard, flat top, fishtail handle	(189)	2000.00
Quart tankard, bud handle terminal	(187)	2000.00
Teapot, pear-shaped, early type	(189)	2500.00

KIRK, ELISHA, York, Pennsylvania, 1785. Very rare.

(190)

5¼"—5½" porringer, solid handle	500.00

KNAPP, ELIJAH, New York City, 1797.
No known examples.

KNEELAND, EDWARD, Boston, Massachusetts, 1768-1791.
No known examples.

KNIGHT, W. W. & CO., Philadelphia, 1840. Britannia. Scarce. Knight
was a merchant rather than a maker.

Teapot	25.00

KRUIGER, LEWIS, Philadelphia, 1830's. Britannia. Plentiful. He made ladles, some of very poor design and quality.

> Ladle, depending upon quality of
> metal and design.   45.00—65.00

*L., M., probably Pennsylvania, early nineteenth century. Rare. These initials, "M.L.," have been found stamped on an English plate.

> Plate   125.00

*L., T., probably Rhode Island, late eighteenth century. Very rare.

> Quart mug   350.00

LAFETRA, MOSES, New York City, 1812-1816. Extremely rare.

(191)

> Pint mug, unique   600.00

LAFETRA and ALLAIRE (Moses Lafetra and Anthony Allaire) New York City, 1816. No known touch of this partnership.

LANGWORTHY, LAWRENCE, Asburton, Devonshire, England, early 1700's. Newport, Rhode Island, 1731-1739. Like most early Boston and Rhode Island pewterers, this man also worked in brass. Several brass pots marked with his initials have been found in Rhode Island. There is at least one pewter plate (in an American collection) bearing his touch, which he is known to have used in England before coming here.

A plate from a home in New England was probably made here, as the English export business was confined to a few well-known makers working in Bristol and London.

(192)

(193)

8″ plate	(193)	1000.00
Pint measure, lidded, balustre		
form, bud thumbpiece (attributed)	(192)	750.00
Brass skillet—footed	(192)	750.00

LANGWORTHY, SOUTHCOTE, Newport, Rhode Island, middle 1700's.
No known examples.

LATHBURY, JOHN, Virginia, 1655.
No known examples.

*LAWRENCE, WILLIAM, Meriden, Connecticut, 1830's. Britannia.
Rare.

*Lamp, patented 1831 and 1834   25.00

LEDDELL, JOSEPH, New York City, 1711-1753. Extremely rare. Also
LEDDELL, JOSEPH, JR., New York City, 1740-1754. The very few
examples extant could be the work of either man.

(194)

Fig. 31: A group of rarities: plate by "HG"; large basin by Joseph Leddell; plate with the "DS" hallmarks of Cornelius Bradford's unknown master, with an unrecorded "London" rose-and-crown touch; quart mug attributed to Horsewell; late eighteenth-century beaker with an unrecorded eagle touch; and a quart mug with Bradford's "DS" hallmarks.

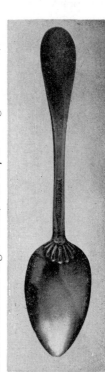

Fig. 32: Rare spoon by Richard Lee.

(195)   (196)

5¼″ porringer,		
crown handle	(196)	850.00
*Quart tankard,		
flat top, crenate lip	(196)	2750.00
Baptismal bowl, multiple		
reed rim, very rare in		
American pewter	(194) 3500.00	(195) 3500.00
9″ plate	(196)	850.00
*13¾″ dish,		
hammered booge	(194)	1100.00
*15″ plate, hammered		
booge	(194)	1500.00
*Covered circular box	(196)	1500.00
19″ plate, hammered		
booge	(194)	3500.00

LEE, RICHARD, *Taunton, Massachusetts, *1770; Grafton, New Hampshire, 1788-1790; Ashfield, Massachusetts, 1791-1793; Lanesborough, Massachusetts, 1794-1802; Springfield, Vermont, 1802-1823.

Also LEE, RICHARD, JR., Springfield, Vermont, 1795-1815; Beverly, Massachusetts, 1816-1820; Rhode Island area, 1820-?.

In most instances, it is not possible to determine which Lee made a given article. The Lees were poor country pewterers, the senior Lee having no formal training, not having served an apprenticeship. Their typical product was the toy, or wine-taster, porringer, 2¼″ size. The variety of handles for these is more varied than those of any other maker. Probably they made their own handle molds of soapstone and discarded them frequently. Almost all their porringers are of the basin type, and the largest (and rarest) is a regular deep 5¾″ basin with a handle attached. Rarity, charm, and distinction of form and design, make Lee pewter a favorite among collectors.

R:Lee   R·L ·   {RICHARD·LEE}

(197)   (198)   (199)

[R.LEE]   {RICHARD·LEE}   LEE

(200)   (201)   (202)   (203)

*5⅜″ plate
(200) 350.00 (202) 375.00
6″ plate
(200) 300.00 (202) 325.00
8¼″ plate
(200) 135.00 (202) 150.00
8⅜″ plate
(200) 135.00 (202) 150.00
4⅜″—11¾″—12¼″ basin
(200) 300.00 (201) 325.00 (202) 300.00
8″ basin
(200) 145.00 (202) 175.00
*3″ beaker
(202) 75.00
Teaspoon
(202) 100.00
Brass skimmer and ladle
(202) 150.00
2¼″ basin porringer; geometric and embossed handles of various designs
(197) 150.00 (198) 160.00 (200) 145.00 (203) 265.00
2¼″ basin porringer, but four handles, unique
(197) 1000.00
2½″—2⅜″—2⅞″ basin porringer
(198) 175.00 (200) 160.00 (201) 160.00 (202) 150.00 (203) 275.00
3⅜″ porringer, three heart handle
(203) 200.00
(One identical porringer has been found in brass with a marked Lee handle.)

3⅜″—3¾″—*4¼″ porringer: conventional, flowered, geometric handles
(199)   225.00 (201) 200.00 (202) 190.00
4¾″—*5″ porringer
(202)   300.00
*5″ range porringer, flowered handle
(202)   350.00
5¾″—5⅞″ basin, flowered porringer handle
(200)   450.00
(Also found with name touch as well as fleur-de-lis touch)
*5½″ porringer, solid handle, embossed sunburst and stars (unmarked)
(199)   200.00
*Tablespoon, beaded edge
(200)   200.00
Quart mug, strap handle
(202)   375.00
*Small teapot, pear-shaped, early type
(200) 2000.00

LEE and CREESY, Beverly, Massachusetts, 1815-1820. Rare. Probably a
partnership of Creesy and Richard Lee, Jr.
See CREESY and LEE.

LEONARD, GUSTAVUS,
See LEONARD, REED, and BARTON.

LEONARD, ZEPHANIAH,
See CROSSMAN, WEST, and LEONARD.

LEONARD, REED, and BARTON (Gustavus Leonard, Henry G. Reed
and Charles E. Barton), Taunton, Massachusetts, 1835-1840. Pewter and
britannia. Plentiful.

Teapot, as to style	35.00—45.00
Tea set	150.00
Coffee pot	40.00
Coffee pot, pigeon-breasted	50.00
Coffee urn, two sizes	75.00—85.00
Chalice, thistle-shape, pair	80.00
Communion flagon	60.00
Lamps, pair	75.00
*Harrison campaign mug, double C handle	65.00

(Only unmarked examples have been found thus far.)

LESLIE, ELKINS, Philadelphia, 1821; Providence, Rhode Island, 1828.
No known examples.

LEWIS, ISAAC C., Meriden, Connecticut, 1834-1852. Britannia. Plentiful.
Also LEWIS, I. C., and CO. Meriden, 1839-1852.
LEWIS and CURTIS (L. J. Curtis), East Meriden, 1836-1839.

2¼″ taster porringer, marked	125.00
2¼″ taster porringer, unmarked	25.00
Teapot, various styles	25.00

Lewis was one of the founders of the Meriden Britannia Company, which
later became the International Silver Company.

LEWIS and COWLES (I. C. LEWIS and GEORGE COWLES), East
Meriden, Connecticut, 1834-1836.

Saucer base candlestick,	
(scarce form; rare when marked):	
Marked	75.00
Unmarked	25.00

LIGHTNER, GEORGE, Baltimore, Maryland, 1806-1815. Plentiful.

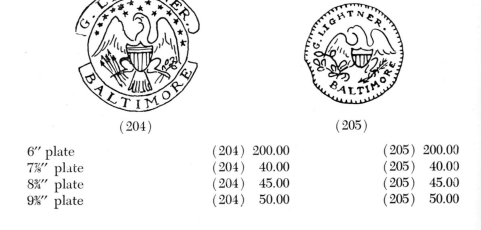

(204)   (205)

6″ plate	(204)	200.00	(205)	200.00
7⅞″ plate	(204)	40.00	(205)	40.00
8¾″ plate	(204)	45.00	(205)	45.00
9⅜″ plate	(204)	50.00	(205)	50.00

11″ deep dish	(204) 65.00	(205) 65.00
13¼″ deep dish	(204) 100.00	(205) 100.00
8″ basin	(204) 60.00	(205) 60.00
10″ basin	(204) 90.00	(205) 90.00
11¾″ basin	(204) 150.00	(205) 150.00

*LINCOLN, probably Hingham, Massachusetts, 1820.

(206)

    *Quart basin, unique   250.00

LINTHWAITE, WILLIAM, Charleston, South Carolina, 1736. No known examples.

*LOESCH, JACOB, Winston-Salem, North Carolina, 1781-1787. No known examples, but known to have made spoons.

LOCKE, J. D., New York City, 1835-1860. Britannia. Scarce.

    Teapot   25.00

LOCKE and CARTER, New York City, 1837-1845. No known examples of this partnership.

*LOVE, in or near Philadelphia, last half of the eighteenth century and early nineteenth. Plentiful. Though most of his pewter is marked "London," there is evidence that it was made in Pennsylvania. Other Philadelphia and Boston pewterers sometimes marked their pewter in this manner, because of a prejudice on the part of their customers for London quality. As in the case of "Semper Eadem," the "Lovebird" touch may well have been a trademark, used by a succession of pewterers. Note the really impressive range of forms.

*Fig. 33: Quart tulip-shaped tankard by "Love." (Courtesy of
the Brooklyn Museum.)*

Fig. 34: Teapot in Queen Anne style by "Love"; unique, and the earliest known form in American teapots. (Courtesy of John F. Ruckman.)

(207)

*6″ plate, smooth rim	200.00
*7⅞″ plate	40.00
*8½″ plate, modified smooth brim	45.00
*8⅝″ deep dish, unusual size	50.00
*11″ deep dish	70.00
*13″ deep dish	125.00
*Large oval platter, extremely rare	750.00

(The only other American example was made by Henry Will.)

*6⅝″ basin	125.00
*6¾″ basin	135.00
*8″ basin	70.00
*10″ basin	100.00
*11½″ basin	175.00
*11½″ basin, hammered	225.00
*12⅜″ basin	250.00
*4¾″ porringer, crown handle	450.00
*Teapot, pear-shaped, early type with fine detail	1000.00
*Teapot, globular shape, true Queen Anne style. Unique in American teapots	2000.00
*Teapot, drum shape	350.00
*Pint mug, straight sides	350.00
*Pint mug, tulip shape, rare form	400.00
*Quart mug, tulip shape	450.00
*Quart tankard, made in plainer Parks Boyd mold	1200.00
*Quart tankard, tulip shape	1200.00
*1¾″ pint balustre measure, lidded, very rare	1200.00

LOVE, I., Baltimore, Maryland, 1840's. Britannia. Scarce.

    Cup and saucer, unique   50.00

LOWE, I., locale unknown. After 1800. Scarce.

*LUCAS, IVORY, New London, Connecticut, 1732-1747, and Ogles Town (Newcastle) Delaware, 1747-1748. Initials in circle touch.
One known example of a spoon is reported. Lucas is reputed to have been a pewterer, brazier, and silversmith.

LYMAN, WILLIAM W., *Wallingford and Meriden, Connecticut, 1844-1852. Britannia. Scarce.

    Teapot, poor design   20.00

LYMAN and COUCH (Ira Couch), Meriden, 1844-1845.
No known examples of this partnership.

MANN, WILLIAM, Boston, 1690-1738.
No known examples.

MANNING, E. B., Middletown, Connecticut, 1850-1875. Britannia. Plentiful. Also used THADDEUS MANNING, and MANNING, BOWMAN and CO. They made chalices, teapots, and many other forms of late design and of no particular interest.

MARSTON, Baltimore, Maryland, 1840's. Britannia. Scarce.

    Lamps, pair   70.00
    Teapot   25.00

MATON, MARCUS, Hartford, Connecticut, 1828. Britannia.
No known examples. Possibly an employee only.

McEUEN, DUNCAN, New York City, 1793-1803.
No known examples.

McEUEN, MALCOLM (See BRADFORD and McEUEN), New York City, 1770-1798.
No known examples.

McEUEN, MALCOLM and SON (Malcolm and Duncan McEuen), New York City, 1793-1798. Extremely rare. Their hallmarks were the "DS" series formerly used by Cornelius Bradford.

(208)

8" plate   400.00
*9¼" plate, smooth brim,
hammered booge   650.00

McILMOY, JOHN, Philadelphia, 1793.
No known examples.

McQUILKIN, WILLIAM, Philadelphia, 1845-1853. Britannia. Plentiful.

Teapot   35.00
Coffee pot   45.00
Water pitcher, 2-quart   65.00
Water pitcher, lidded   85.00
Water pitcher, gallon   150.00
*Baptismal bowl   150.00

MELVILLE, ANDREW, Newport, Rhode Island, 1804-1810.
No known examples.

MELVILLE, DAVID, Newport, Rhode Island, 1755-1793. Scarce, except in flatware.

(209)

(210)

(211)

(212)

D ✕ M
1788

(213)

(214)

(215)

(216)

6⅛″ plate
  (212) 350.00 (216) 250.00
8¼″-8½″ plate
  (210) 250.00 (212) 250.00 (214) 50.00 (216) 45.00
8⅞″ plate
  (210) 135.00 (214) 60.00 (216) 55.00
12³⁄₁₆″ platter
  (214) 95.00 (216) 90.00
14″ platter, rare size
  (214) 225.00 (216) 200.00
3¾″ basin, rare
  (209) 500.00 (214) 350.00
8″ basin
  (214) 75.00 (216) 70.00
8⅞″ basin
  (211) 350.00 (214) 95.00 (216) 90.00
4⅝″ porringer, flowered handle, scarce size
  (216) 250.00
Porringer, 5″ range
  (214) 235.00 (215) 235.00 (216) 235.00
Porringer, 5¼″ range, geometric handle, unique
  (211) 350.00 (215) 325.00
Porringer, crown handle, very rare
  (215) 325.00
Porringer, solid handle
  (209) 500.00 (210) 400.00 (213) 500.00 (214) 235.00 (216) 235.00
*Quart mug, strap handle
  (214) 475.00

MELVILLE, SAMUEL, Newport, Rhode Island, 1793-1800. Very scarce.
He was the son of David, and his touch is sometimes found in conjunction
with that of his father.

S M

(217)

5¼″ porringer, solid handle,
initials cast on bracket   325.00

MELVILLE, S. & T., (SAMUEL and THOMAS), Newport, Rhode
Island, 1793-1800. Scarce. Nephews to David Melville.

(218)

7¹¹⁄₁₆″ and 8⅜″ plate   175.00
12″ dish   190.00
6½″ basin   300.00
8⅞″ basin   200.00

MELVILLE, THOMAS, Newport, Rhode Island, 1793-1796. Rare.

Also MELVILLE II, THOMAS, Newport, Rhode Island, 1796-1824.
Though it is difficult to distinguish between the work of these two men,
it is believed that the first touch below is that of Thomas Melville and
the second group the touches of Thomas II.

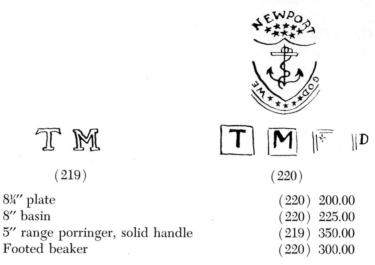

(219)   (220)

8¼″ plate	(220) 200.00
8″ basin	(220) 225.00
5″ range porringer, solid handle	(219) 350.00
Footed beaker	(220) 300.00

The first touch above is found in conjunction with the anchor touch of David Melville.

*MELVILLE, WILLIAM L., Newport, Rhode Island, 1805-1810. Extremely rare. Anchor touch.

NEWPORT

(221)

*8″ plate, hammered booge
(only known example)   350.00

MERIDEN BRITANNIA COMPANY, Meriden, Connecticut, 1852-?
Britannia. Plentiful.

This company made teapots, lamps, candlesticks, dishes and other articles of late form, which are of little value or interest to collectors.

MERRYFIELD, ROBERT, New York City, 1760.
No known examples.

MICHEL, ANDRE, New York City, 1795-1797.
No known examples.

*MILLER, JOSIAH, New England, 1750-1775(?). Scarce. This man made pewter sundials and buttons. The dials are marked with either full name or initial touches in raised letters; one bronze example is known.

    Sundial, various sizes, 4″ and larger   85.00

MINZE, JAMES
See STAFFORD, SPENCER.

*MIX, G. I. and CO. Yalesville (Wallingford), Connecticut, 1860's.
Common.

    *Tablespoon   7.50

*MIX, WILLIAM, Spoonville (East Granby), Connecticut, 1820-1840.
Britannia. Scarce.

    *Tablespoon, several types, marked
    WM. MIX in rectangle   10.00

MOLINEUX, GEORGE
See CAPEN and MOLINEUX.

MOORE, LUKE, Philadelphia, 1819-1822.
No known examples.

MOREY and OBER; MOREY, OBER and CO.; MOREY and SMITH (David B. Morey, R. H. Ober, and Thomas Smith), Boston, 1852-1855. Common. A group of related partnerships. They made britannia, with a few exceptions, of poor design.

Lamp, as to style and size	15.00—25.00
Teapot	25.00
*½-pint handled beaker,	
1825 design	45.00
Pint mug	45.00
Candlesticks, pair	60.00

MORGAN, HENRY, Groton, Connecticut, 1849. Britannia.
No known examples.

MUNSON, JOHN, Yalesville (Wallingford), Connecticut, 1846-1852.
Britannia. Common.

Teapot, late and poor form	20.00

N., W., New England, 1800. These initials are cast on the underside of
finely molded crown handled porringer handles. Very scarce.

4⅝″ porringer, crown handle	50.00
Same, with broad spline on under side of handle	55.00
5″ porringer, crown handle	65.00

N. ENGLAND, in rectangle.
See MELVILLE, DAVID.

NEAL, I., New England or New York City, 1842. Britannia. Scarce.
    Neal was a maker of unusual "pump" lamps, with saucer bases,
marked in circle with name, patent, and date touch. The same form is
also found with only a "patent" touch in rectangle.

Lamp	60.00

*NICHOLS, O., New England, 1820. An eight-inch basin has been found
with a rectangular name touch of this maker, the only one reported so far.

*8″ basin, unique	200.00

NORRIS, GEORGE.
See OSTRANDER and NORRIS.

NORSWORTH, JOHN, Norfolk, Virginia, 1771.
No known examples.

Fig. 35: All excellent forms, mostly eighteenth century, mostly unmarked. Top row: shaker; sugar bowl, Philadelphia; creamer, New York City, probably by John Will; bowl, New York City, probably by Henry Will; creamer, Philadelphia, perhaps by William Will; sugar bowl, Philadelphia, also probably by William Will. Bottom row: beaker, Connecticut, probably Danforth; chalice, Hartford, Boardman, nineteenth century; bowl, Philadelphia, nineteenth century; sugar bowl, early nineteenth century; bowl, Philadelphia, early nineteenth century; baptismal bowl, early nineteenth century; engraved mug, Hartford, Boardman. (All from the collection of John F. Ruckman.)

NORTH and ROWE (John North and Adna S. Rowe) Augusta, Georgia, 1818-1823. Emigrant Connecticut pewterers.
No known examples.

NORTHEY, DAVID, Salem, Massachusetts, 1732-1778.
No known examples.

NORTHEY, WILLIAM, Lynn, Massachusetts, 1764-1804.
No known examples.

NOTT, WILLIAM (*See also* JOHNSON, JEHIEL), Middletown, Connecticut, 1813-1817; Fayetteville, North Carolina, 1817-1825. Very rare.

(222)

7⅞″-8¹³⁄₁₆″ plate	200.00
7⅞″-8¹³⁄₁₆″ plate	225.00
*11³⁄₁₆″ platter, very rare	300.00
11¼″ deep dish	250.00
13⅛″ deep dish	325.00

NOTT, BABCOCK, & JOHNSON (William Nott, Samuel Babcock and Jehiel Johnson), Middletown, Connecticut, 1817.
No known examples.

OBER, R. H.
See MOREY and OBER.

OLCOTT, J. W. (or J. WOLCOTT), Baltimore, Maryland, early 1800's.
Very rare.

(223)

    8″ plate   200.00

OSTRANDER, CHARLES, New York City, 1848-1854. Britannia.
Plentiful.

    Also OSTRANDER and NORRIS (George Norris), New York City,
1848-1850. Britannia. Plentiful.

    Lamp, as to style and size   25.00 —35.00
    Candlesticks, pair   75.00

P., C., New England, 1800. Porringers are found with these initials cast
on the bracket.

    Porringer, 4″ range, Old English handle, rare   75.00

PALETHORP, JOHN H. (J. H. PALETHORP and COMPANY; R. and
J. H. PALETHORP; PALETHORP and CONNELL), Philadelphia, 1820-
1840.
Pewter, later britannia. Scarce.
Rectangular name and place touches.

    8″ tablespoon   45.00
    Ladle   90.00
    Beaker, small   45.00
    Waste bowl   75.00
    Teapot   65.00
    Water pitcher   85.00
    Mug, pint   200.00
    *Chalice 7⁹⁄₁₆″, tall, unique   225.00

PALETHORP, ROBERT, JR., Philadelphia, 1817-1822. Scarce. No special value should be attached to any particular touch.

<table>
(224)   (225)
</table>

7¾″-8¼″ plate	50.00
9″ plate	60.00
13″ deep dish	110.00
13½″ platter	125.00
10″ basin	90.00
11⅜″ basin	150.00
Pint mug	225.00
Quart mug	225.00
Pint mug, barrel shape, rare	400.00
Pint infusion pot, rare	650.00
Spoon, dessert	75.00

PARKER, CHARLES G. and CO., Meriden, Connecticut, 1849. Britannia. Scarce.

Tablespoon	8.00

PARKER, J. G., Rochester, New York, 1840. Britannia. Scarce.

Lamp	25.00

PARKIN, W. New England, 1830's. Britannia. Scarce.

Footed creamer	35.00
Teapot, oval, footed, engraved	75.00
Teapot	30.00

PARMENTER, W. H., probably New England, 1840's. Britannia. Rare.

    Lamp   25.00

PASCHALL, THOMAS, Philadelphia, 1686-1718.
No known examples.

PAVEY, GEORGE, Boston, 1733.
No known examples.

PEARSE (PIERCY), ROBERT, New York City, 1790's.
No known examples.

PEEL, HENRY, Philadelphia, 1822-1833.
No known examples.

*PENNOCK, SIMON, East Marlborough, Pennsylvania, 1805-1815, and
Lancaster County, Pennsylvania, 1817-1845. Extremely rare.
    The first touch shown may be that of his father, Samuel Pennock.

(226)

(227)

*Porringer, tab handle,
5″ range   (226) 350.00   (227) 325.00
*Large plate, two sizes   (226) 250.00

PIERCE, SAMUEL, Greenfield, Massachusetts, 1792-1830. Scarce.
*(Samuel Pierce, Jr., may also have made pewter).

(228)

(229)

(230)

*6″ plate	(229)	375.00				
8″ plate	(228)	60.00	(229)	60.00	(230)	45.00
11¼″ dish	(228)	75.00	(229)	75.00	(230)	70.00
13″ deep dish	(228)	150.00	(229)	150.00	(230)	125.00
12³⁄₁₆″ platter	(228)	125.00	(229)	125.00	(230)	100.00
8″ basin	(228)	75.00	(230)	65.00		
Beaker, squat, 3⅝-4″ range	(229)	225.00—250.00				
Pint mug	(229)	250.00				
Quart mug	(228)	275.00	(229)	250.00		
Baptismal bowl	(230)	400.00				
*Teapot, late pear-shaped	(229)	250.00				
*4″ porringer, Old English handle	(229)	350.00				
*5¼″ porringer, Old English handle	(229)	350.00				
2½″ silhouette frame, unmarked		35.00				
*Open salt, unique	(229)	450.00				

PLUMLY, CHARLES, Providence, Rhode Island, 1829; Middletown, Connecticut, 1844-1848.
No known examples.

PLUMLY and BIDGOOD (Charles Plumly and Bidgood), Philadelphia, 1825. Probably the same Plumly as listed above. Extremely rare.

(231)

8″ plate	300.00
Pint mug	500.00

*PLUMLY and FELTON, Possibly Philadelphia, 1840. Rare.

    Tall teapot   65.00

POMROY, WILLIAM C., (Associated with STALKAMP, J. H. and COMPANY.)

PORTER, ALLEN, Westbrook, Maine, 1830-1840. Britannia. Scarce.
    Also PORTER, A. and F., Westbrook, Maine. No known touch is attributable to the partnership.

*Teapot, late pear-shaped	125.00
Teapot, other styles	25.00— 35.00
Tall coffee pot	60.00
Coffee pot, small, two styles	30.00
Lamps, pair	45.00

PORTER, FREEMAN, Westbrook, Maine, 1835-1860's. Britannia. Common.

Teapot	25.00
Tall coffee pot	45.00
6¼″ candlesticks, pair	70.00
6½″ candlestick with saucer base, very rare	125.00
Lamps, pair	75.00
2-quart water pitcher	50.00

PORTER, JAMES, Connecticut Valley, 1795-1803; Baltimore, Maryland, 1803. Very rare.

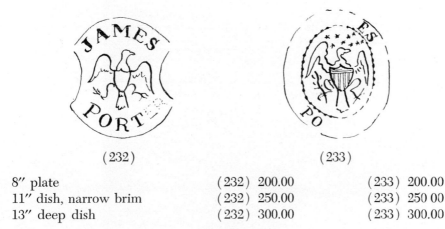

     (232)   (233)

8″ plate	(232) 200.00	(233) 200.00
11″ dish, narrow brim	(232) 250.00	(233) 250 00
13″ deep dish	(232) 300.00	(233) 300.00

Fig. 36: Marked porringers showing diversity of handles. Top row: dolphin handle by the Norwich and Hartford Danforths; three Old English handles by the Bassetts; geometric handle by Richard Lee; solid handle by the Melvilles; solid handle by Robert Porter. Bottom row: flowered handle from Rhode Island; crown handle by John Danforth; crown handle by David Melville; small porringer below with embossed handle and the third example from the right, both by Richard Lee; the remainder by Thomas D. Boardman.

PORTER, JEPTHA
See KILBOURN, SAMUEL.

*PORTER, ROBERT, Caln Township, Chester County, Pennsylvania, 1780's.

He is definitely known to have had molds for tab-handled porringers. There are several examples of porringers with a large "P" on the handle, which might be attributed to him.

(234)

*5½″ porringer, tab handle	250.00

*PORTER, SAMUEL, Taunton, Mass., 1800.

Quart mug	300.00

POTTER, W., probably New England, 1830's. Britannia. Rare.

Sand shaker, rare form in pewter	125.00
Sand shaker, unmarked	60.00

PUTNAM, JAMES H. (*See also* BAILEY and PUTNAM), Malden, Massachusetts, 1830-1835. Britannia. Plentiful.

5″ plate, very early form, rare	200.00
Teapot, as to style	25.00—50.00
Lamps, as to size and style, pair	60.00—75.00
Candlesticks, pair	60.00
Small lamp, saucer base	20.00
Water pitcher	50.00
10″ demi-john, Continental in style, unique in marked American pewter	250.00

RAISIN, GEORGE, Boston, 1718-1728.
No known examples.

*RAND, EDWARD, Newburyport, Massachusetts, 1794-180-?.
No known examples.

RANDLE (or RANDALL), JOHN, Boston, Massachusetts, 1738-1739.
No known examples.

REED, HENRY G., (*See also* LEONARD, REED, and BARTON),
Taunton, Massachusetts, 1840. Britannia. Very rare. LEONARD, REED,
and BARTON, and REED and BARTON made similar products, but
later and less desirable.

Tea pot	50.00
Coffee Pot	75.00

REICH, JOHN PHILIP, Salem, North Carolina, 1820-1830. Extremely
rare.

(235)

8¾″ plate, unique	500.00
*8″ basin, unique	600.00

REICH, J. and P. (John and Philip Reich), Salem, North Carolina, 1829.
No known examples of this partnership.

RENTON and CO., New York City, 1830's. Britannia. Rare.

Saucer base miniature lamp	35.00

RICHARDSON, FRANCIS B., Providence, Rhode Island, 1847-1848.
No known examples.

RICHARDSON, GEORGE, Sr., Boston, Massachusetts, 1818-1828; Cranston, Rhode Island, 1828-1845. His earlier Boston name touch is rare and
deserves a twenty-five percent premium over the later marks. This man's
sugar bowls, of very good design, are pictured on the frontispiece of
J. B. Kerfoot's *American Pewter,* and command a very high price.

G.RICHARDSON
BOSTON

(236)

CRANSTON R.I.

(237)

9⅝″ deep dish, Boston touch	125.00
*11¾″ wash bowl, Boston touch,	
extremely rare in pewter	350.00
Pint mug, Boston touch, late style handle	125.00
Shaving mug, Boston touch, very rare form	250.00
Sugar bowl	350.00
*Sugar bowl with hinged cover	200.00
*Waste bowl made from above	
mold (only one reported)	200.00
Teapot, conforming to sugar bowl	75.00
Teapot, pear-shaped	150.00
Teapot, pear-shaped, with	
base extended	250.00
10¾″ teapot, lighthouse	100.00
Teapot, other forms, depending on	
size and touch	35.00— 75.00
Coffee pot	65.00
*Cream pitcher	100.00
Water pitcher, open	65.00
Water pitcher, lidded	85.00
Water pitcher, japanned, very rare	250.00
*Tablespoon, shell drop	85.00

RICHARDSON, GEORGE B. Jr., Providence, Rhode Island, 1847-1848.
Britannia.
No known examples.

ROGERS, JOHN, Philadelphia, 1840. Britannia.
No known examples.

ROGERS, SMITH and CO., Hartford, Connecticut, 1850's. Britannia. Scarce.

> Chalices, pair   60.00

ROWE, ADNA S.
See NORTH and ROWE.

RUSSELL and BEACH, Chester, Connecticut, 1838. Britannia. No known examples.

*RUST, H. N., probably New York City, 1840. Extremely rare.

H.N.RUST

(238)

> *8″ basin, cast pewter,
> an early form by a late
> maker, unique   100.00

RUST, JOHN N. and SAMUEL, New York City, 1842-1845. Britannia. No known examples.

RUST, LEONARD, M., New York City, 1849. Britannia. No known examples.

RUST, SAMUEL, New York City, 1837-1845. Britannia. Scarce.

> Lamp   35.00

*S., B. G. and CO., Northeastern Massachusetts, 1825-1830. Extremely rare.

│B.G.S. & Co.│

(239)

> *5″ beaker, tastefully bright-cut   100.00
> *Snuff box 2¾″ x ¾″ deep, bright-cut   200.00

*S., H., probably Virginia, mid-eighteenth century. Extremely rare.

One plate of probable American manufacture, with initials cast in cartouche on the underside of the brim, recorded. Some Virginia plates are marked in this manner.

*9″ plate, smooth brim	200.00

*S., I., with rose and crown. (*See* SEMPER EADEM, B., R., and SKINNER, JOHN).

S., T., New England, second half of eighteenth century. Rare. While many examples have been found in the western Connecticut and Hudson Valley areas, an equal number have been found around Boston. The newly found dated touch is one of the few known American examples.

TS

(240)

*Pint mug, tulip-shaped rare form, dated 1759	450.00
Quart mug, tulip-shaped	350.00
Quart tankard, tulip-shaped	1000.00

SAGE, TIMOTHY, St. Louis, 1840's. Britannia. Scarce. Also SAGE, T. and CO.; SAGE and BEEBE.

Teapot	35.00
Water pitcher	45.00
Miniature pitcher, (the smallest one known, 5½″, lidded)	200.00
Miniature pitcher, unmarked	75.00

SAVAGE, WILLIAM, Middletown, Connecticut, late 1830's. Britannia. Also SAVAGE and GRAHAM; GRAHAM and SAVAGE.
Successors to William Danforth.

*Covered syrup pitcher	45.00
Teapot	35.00
*Ladle	65.00

Fig. 37: "Semper Eadem" Boston touch with "London"
scroll used by John Skinner.

*Fig. 38: "I.S." rose-and-crown touch with "Semper Eadem."
The John Skinner initials together with his known "London"
touch would seem to identify him as the user of the
mysterious Latin touch.*

SCHMIDT, T. Possibly Connecticut, 1870's. Britannia.

Spoon   5.00

SEIP, JACOB, Philadelphia, 1820-1822.
No known examples.

SELLEW & CO., (Enos, Osman, and William Sellew), Cincinnati, Ohio,
1830-1860. Britannia. Common.

Though late, this firm made pewter and britannia of excellent design.

8″ candlesticks, balustre turned, pair	75.00
Candlesticks, same but 10″	95.00
Candlesticks, unmarked, as to size	35.00— 45.00
8″ plate, eagle touch	100.00
12³⁄₁₆″ plate, smooth rim	150.00
13″ deep dish, smooth brim	175.00
Tea set	125.00
Lamps, pair	80.00
Communion set	150.00
Teapot, late pear-shaped	135.00

SELTZER, ABRAHAM, Philadelphia, 1793.
No known examples.

SEMPER EADEM, (See also SKINNER, JOHN, and B., R.), Boston,
Massachusetts, second half of eighteenth century. Scarce. This touch is
a trade mark, rather than the touch of a single pewterer. The "Boston"
and two "London" touches were used by a succession of Boston pewterers. The last touch shown, bearing the "IS" initials, indicates that John
Skinner was one of the pewterers using this touch.

(241)

(242)

(243)

(244)

*7¾″ plate	(241)	80.00	(242)	90.00	(243)	200.00
7⅞″ plate	(241)	80.00	(242)	90.00		
8¼″ plate	(241)	85.00	(242)	95.00		
12¼″ platter	(241)	125.00	(242)	145.00		
*13½″ platter	(242)	175.00				
15″ platter	(241)	200.00	(242)	225.00	(244)	225
*16⅜″ platter, unique	(244)	800.00				
*9½″ deep dish, smooth brim, hammered booge	(244)	250.00				
*6″ basin	(241)	200.00				
8″ basin	(241)	1000.00				
*Quart mug, strap handle	(244)	450.00				
*Quart tankard	(244)	1750.00				

SHAW
See SICKEL and SHAW

SHELDON and FELTMAN (Smith Sheldon and James C. Feltman, Jr.) Albany, New York, 1847-1848. Britannia. Common. All their products were late in form and inferior in design.

Teapot	25.00
Coffee pot	40.00
Communion flagon	50.00
10″ deep dish	25.00

SHOFF, L., Lancaster County, Pennsylvania, 1780's. Extremely rare.

(245)

11" dish, smooth brim,
hammered booge   350.00

SHRIMPTON, HENRY, Boston, 1615-1666.
Also SHRIMPTON, SAMUEL (son); SHRIMPTON, HENRY (nephew);
SHRIMPTON, JONATHAN, d. 1674.

No known examples, although a 9" plate with initials "HS" cast under
the brim has been attributed to Henry Shrimpton.

SICKEL and SHAW (H. G. Sickel and Shaw), Philadelphia, 1850-1854.
Britannia. Rare.

Lamp   25.00

SIMPKINS, THOMAS, Boston, 1727-1766. Extremely rare.

(246)	(247)

8" plate   (247) 600.00
8½" plate   (246) 600.00

SIMPSON, SAMUEL, Yalesville, Connecticut, 1835-1852.
Also SIMPSON and BENHAM (Morris Benham), New York City, 1845-
1847. Britannia. Scarce.

Teapot   25.00

SKINNER, JOHN, Boston, 1760-1790. Scarce.
(See also SEMPER EADEM).

Skinner was perhaps the most productive of the eighteenth-century
Boston pewterers. At times, he marked his pewter with a "London"
touch. Plates with hammered booge are probably pre-Revolutionary in
period.

Fig. 39: Boston pewter. The rare strap-handle pint mugs have moon-and-star handle terminals, and were probably made by John Skinner, though unmarked. The three plates on the left have the "Semper Eadem" touch used by Skinner; the smallest, a rare small plate of 7⅝" diameter, also has the "RB" rose-and-crown touch. The extremely rare 16⅝" large plate bears the "IS—Semper Eadem" rose-and-crown touch; this is one of two known Boston plates exceeding fifteen inches in diameter. Flanking it are 9" and 9½" smooth-brim Skinner plates. The quart basin has the mark of "Semper Eadem."

The hitherto unreported combination of the "Skinner" and "Semper Eadem" touches, indicates that he was one, if not the only, user of the latter touch.

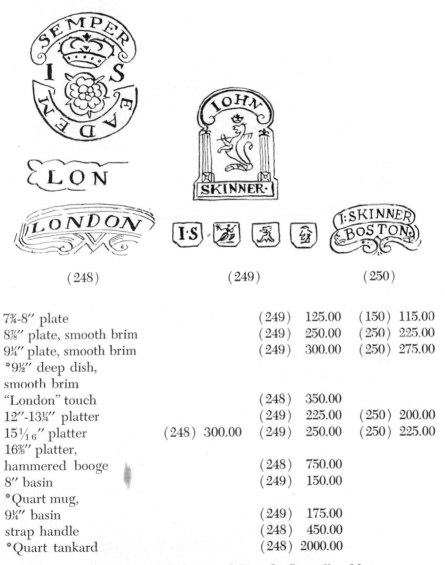

(248)   (249)   (250)

7¾-8″ plate		(249) 125.00	(150) 115.00
8⅞″ plate, smooth brim		(249) 250.00	(250) 225.00
9¼″ plate, smooth brim		(249) 300.00	(250) 275.00
*9½″ deep dish, smooth brim			
"London" touch		(248) 350.00	
12″-13¼″ platter		(249) 225.00	(250) 200.00
15¹⁄₁₆″ platter	(248) 300.00	(249) 250.00	(250) 225.00
16⅜″ platter, hammered booge		(248) 750.00	
8″ basin		(249) 150.00	
*Quart mug,			
9¼″ basin		(249) 175.00	
strap handle		(248) 450.00	
*Quart tankard		(248) 2000.00	

For items with unrecorded curved "London" scroll, add twenty percent.

SMITH, EBEN, Beverly, Massachusetts, *1813-1856. Britannia. Common.
Recent evidence moves Smith's working dates back some thirty years.

Teapot	35.00
Teapot, pigeon-breasted	50.00
*Teapot, pear-shaped	150.00
Coffee pot, lighthouse	45.00
Coffee pot, pigeon-breasted	45.00
Communion flagon	125.00
*Covered box, possibly a tinder box	200.00
Lamps, pair, depending on size and style	65.00— 80.00
Candlesticks, pair	75.00
Castor holder	35.00

SMITH, THOMAS, Boston, 1700-1742.
No known examples.

SMITH, WILLIAM R., Middletown, Connecticut, 1848. Britannia.
No known examples.

*SMITH, WILLIAM & Brother, Stafford County, Virginia, 1774. They
were makers of molds.
No known examples.

SMITH, OBER and CO.; THOMAS SMITH and CO.; SMITH and CO.;
SMITH and OBER. (See MOREY and OBER). These were a close and
rapid succession of partnerships, making the same products.

SMITH and CO.; SMITH and FELTMAN. (See SHELDON and FELT-
MAN). Related partnerships with the same products.
No known examples bearing the touch of this SMITH and CO.

SOUTHMAYD, EBENEZER, Middletown, Connecticut, 1790's. Castleton, Vermont, 1802-1830. Extremely rare.

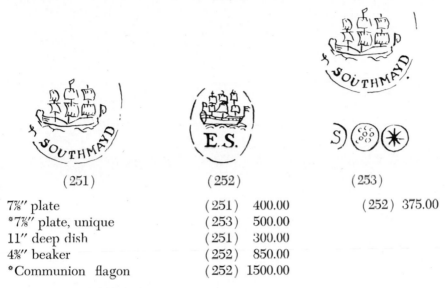

(251)   (252)   (253)

7⅞" plate	(251) 400.00	(252) 375.00
*7⅞" plate, unique	(253) 500.00	
11" deep dish	(251) 300.00	
4⅜" beaker	(252) 850.00	
*Communion flagon	(252) 1500.00	

SPENCER, GEORGE B.;
Also SPENCER, THOMAS (*See* STAFFORD, SPENCER)

STAFFORD, SPENCER, Albany, New York, 1794-1830. Plentiful.
Related partnerships:

SPENCER, STAFFORD and CO.;
STAFFORD, S., and CO.;
STAFFORD and MINZE;
STAFFORD, BENEDICT and CO.;
STAFFORD, ROGERS and CO.;
STAFFORD, HALLENBAKE; JOAB, JOHN;
STAFFORD, SPENCER, and SPENCER, JR.

This man was a highly successful merchant. The pewter marked with his name was made by such able Albany pewterers as Peter Young and Timothy Brigden. He employed many journeyman pewterers in his shop.

The "S. Stafford" touch is sometimes found alone. Plates bearing Peter Young and Henry Will rose and crown marks, along with the Stafford name touch, usually have a hammered booge. Such pieces should bring about thirty percent more.

S.STAFFORD

(254)

S.STAFFORD

(255)

S.STAFFORD   ALBANY   ALBANY

(256)   (257)   (258)

7¾" plate	(255)	85.00	(256)	80.00	(257) 45.00	(258) 40.00
8⅜" plate	(225)	90.00	(257)	55.00		
13½" deep dish	(255)	100.00	(256)	110.00	(257) 50.00	
6⅝" basin	(257)	135.00	(258)	125.00		
8" basin	(256)	80.00	(257)	60.00		
10½" basin	(257)	80.00	(258)	60.00		
*Teapot, drum-shaped	(257)	300.00				
*Teapot, pear-shaped	(257)	200.00				
*Teapot, pear-shaped, late type, very large	(257)	150.00				

Quart mug   (257)   275.00
Quart
tankard,
Young
style   (257) 1400.00
*Com-
munion
flagon   (254)   400.00   (257) 350.00

STALKAMP, J. H. and CO., Cincinnati, Ohio, 1850's. Britannia. Scarce.

    Teapot   25.00
    Lamp   25.00

STANDISH, ALEXANDER, Probably New England, 1840's. Britannia.
Rare. Possibly he is the Standish of ARMITAGE and STANDISH.

    Coffee urn   125.00

STARR, WILLIAM, H., New York City, 1843-1846. Britannia. Rare.

    Small nursing lamp   25.00

STEDMAN, S., Eastern Connecticut or Rhode Island, 1800. Rare.

    Ladle, pewter, with wooden handle   150.00
    Ladle, unmarked   35.00

STEINMAN, JOHN FREDERICK, Lancaster, Pennsylvania, 1783-1785.
No known examples.

*STEPHENSON, HENRY, Taunton, Massachusetts, 1818.
No known examples.

*STIMPSON, JAMES, Baltimore, Maryland, 1840's. Britannia. Very rare.

    *Communion flagon   100.00
    *Teapot   45.00

*STEVENS, C., Connecticut Valley, 1760. Extremely rare. The author has
had a bronze button mold made by this man.

STODDART, FREDERICK, Philadelphia, 1833.
No known examples.

*STRANGE, JOSEPH, Taunton, Massachusetts, 1800.
No known examples.

SUMNER, WILLIAM F.
See ENDICOTT and SUMNER.

SYKES, probably Connecticut, 1840's. Britannia. Very rare.

    Pocket flask   95.00

TAUNTON BRITANNIA MANUFACTURING CO., Taunton, Massachusetts, 1830-1835. Britannia. Common. This company made some of the most beautiful lamps in American pewter.

Lamp, miniature, saucer base, each	30.00
Lamps, pair, as to size and style	60.00—90.00
Teapot	35.00
Coffee pot	45.00
Coffee pot, pigeon-breasted	45.00
Sugar bowl	35.00
Creamer	35.00
Candlesticks, pair, as to size and style	40.00—60.00

*THOMAS, JOHN, Shippen Lane, Pennsylvania, and Trenton, New Jersey, 1841. Britannia. Rare.

*Teapot	50.00
*Spoon	10.00

*THOMPSON, ANDREW, Albany, New York, 1810-1820. Extremely rare.

(259)

*8″ plate	250.00
*8″ basin	300.00

THORNTON, JOHN, probably Pennsylvania, after 1774. No known examples.

Fig. 40: Normal flatware gateway and hallmark touches of
John Skinner of Boston.

Fig. 41: Rhode Island anchor touch on a unique plate by Tillinghast. This is an old Providence name, but some of the family moved to Fayetteville, N. C., a center of southern pewter-making, in the early nineteenth century.

*TILLINGHAST, Providence, Rhode Island, or Fayetteville, North Carolina, 1810. Unique. Note Rhode Island anchor touch.

(260)

    *8" plate   350.00

TOMLINSON, locale unknown, 1843. Britannia. Rare.

    Lamp   35.00

TRASK, ISRAEL, Beverly, Massachusetts, *1807-1856. Pewter and britannia. Common. Note the change in his working dates. No special value should be attached to touch. Trask was a maker of unusual ability, undoubtedly due in part to his early training as a silversmith. His tall, engraved, lighthouse teapots and his Federal-style teapots are among the best of the period, as are those of his contemporaries, Oliver Trask and Eben Smith.

(261)   (262)

Lamps, as to size and style, pair	60.00— 90.00
Castor set (with bottles)	45.00
Castor, frame only	15.00
*Chalices, pewter, 5¼", pair	95.00
*Chalices, 5¾", pair	75.00
*Chalice, two handled, britannia, formed in the manner of silver, unusual technique for a pewterer	200.00
*4" beaker	65.00
Communion flagon, engraved bands	100.00
*Communion flagon, triple C strap handle	150.00

Fig. 42: A representative group of pieces, dating from the late seventeenth century to the mid-nineteenth century. Candlesticks by Dunham, 1840; lamp by Endicott and Sumner, 1835; flagon, unknown maker "HI," 1750; 8" plate and pint mug by Samuel Pierce, 1800; sugar bowl by George Richardson, 1830; seventeenth-century platter by the Dolbeares; unique tea-tile by Dunham, 1840; engraved teapot by Trask, 1820; plate by Richard Lee, 1800; beaker by Trask; "lighthouse" tall pot by Charles Yale, 1820; reading lamp with bulls-eye magnifying lenses by Gleason, 1840; candlesticks by Hopper, 1850.

    *Beaker, handled   50.00

    10¾″ baptismal bowl   250.00

    Teapot, oval, Federal style, engraved,

    sometimes with ball feet   200.00

    *Teapot, oval touch   225.00

    Creamer, for above   60.00

    *Teapot, boat-shaped, very rare form   200.00

    10″-12″ lighthouse teapot, engraved bands   75.00

    *Sander, very rare form in American pewter   125.00

TRASK, JOHN, probably Beverly, Massachusetts, early 1800's. Very rare.

    *Pewter buckles, pair (initials "JT" cast in back)   50.00

TRASK, OLIVER, Beverly, Massachusetts, 1825 through 1830's. Scarce.

[O.TRASK]

(263)

    10″-12″ lighthouse teapot, engraved banding   65.00

    Teapot, oval, engraved   150.00

    Teapot, others   35.00

    Squat beaker   95.00

    5″ range beaker   95.00

    Lidded box   150.00

    10¾″ baptismal bowl, a superb form   250.00

    12″ large spouted Communion flagon,

    on pedestal base, unusual form   150.00

    12″ Communion flagon, conventional base,

    expanded bands near base and top,

    double C handle   150.00

    *Communion plate   60.00

TREADWAY, AMOS, Middletown, Connecticut, 1760-1790. Very rare.

(264)   (265)

7⅞" plate   (264) 200.00   (265) 150.00
12³⁄₁₆" platter   (265) 200.00
*13" deep dish   (264) 300.00   (265) 250.00

TYLER, JOHN, Boston, 1720-1756.
No known examples.

TYMIESEN, SEBASTIAN, a partner in STAFFORD, SPENCER and
COMPANY, which see.

*UFEN, J. M., probably Pennsylvania, eighteenth century. Very rare.

  *7" trifid end spoon   100.00

UVEN, M. B., same as above. (Ufen, J. M.)

  *7" spoon, same mold as above   100.00

*VAN NORDEN, PETER, Bound Brook, New Jersey, 1782.
No known examples.

VOSE and COMPANY, Albany, New York, 1840's. Britannia. Scarce.

  Teapot   25.00
  Lamps, pair   75.00

*W., B., Rhode Island or eastern Massachusetts, early 1800's. Very rare.

  *Ladle, large, all pewter   65.00

W., E. (in a cartouche)
See WILLETT, EDWARD.

*W., E., probably New England, early nineteenth century. Initials cast in porringer handle.

    *3⁷⁄₁₆″ porringer, heart and crescent handle   75.00

W., I., possibly New England, third quarter of eighteenth century. Extremely rare.

(266)

    5¼″ porringer, geometric handle   350.00
    Tall beaker   450.00

WADSWORTH, LESTER, Hartford, Connecticut, 1838. Britannia. No known examples. Possibly an employee only.

WALLACE, R. and COMPANY, Wallingford, Connecticut, 1855. Britannia. Scarce. At first they made spoons, later plated and sterling articles.

    Spoon   8.00

WARD, H. B. and COMPANY, Wallingford, Connecticut, late 1840's. Britannia. Scarce.

    Teapot   25.00

WARREN, New England or New York, 1840. Britannia. Rare.

    Lamp (marked "Warrens Hard Metal")   40.00

WAYNE, C. P. and Son, Philadelphia, 1835. Britannia. Rare.

    Teapot   45.00

*WEBB, W., New York City, 1810-1820's. Rare. The author has owned two candle molds with "W. Webb, N. Y." cast in.

    *Candle mold, pewter tubes in wooden frame   65.00

WEEKES, JAMES, New York City and Poughkeepsie, New York, 1820-1835; also WEEKES, J. and COMPANY. Pewter and britannia. Common. Except as noted, items are britannia.

8″ basin, cast pewter	100.00
3″ beaker	45.00
Ladle, cast pewter	65.00
Spoon	20.00
Lamps, as to size and style, pair	65.00— 90.00
Candlestick, as to size	60.00— 80.00
Salt, cast pewter	125.00
*Teapot	65.00

WENDELIN, JOHN F., partner in STALKAMP, J. H. and COMPANY, which see.

WEST, WILLIAM A.
See CROSSMAN, WEST, and LEONARD.

WHITCOMB, A. G., Boston, 1820's and 1830's. Scarce.

*Inkwell, small desk size	15.00
Inkwell, large	75.00
Inkstand, two drawers below well; unique in American pewter	300.00

WHITE, H., a partner in SMITH and COMPANY, Boston.

WHITEHOUSE, E., locale unknown, early 1800's. Scarce.

Spoon, as to size and form, rectangle name touch	7.50—12.00
Spoon, with patriotic decoration, rare	75.00

*WHITEHOUSE and WOODBURY, locale unknown, 1840's. Rare. This partnership could conceivably be English.

*Teapot, boat-shaped	65.00

WHITFIELD, GEORGE, New York City, 1836-1865.
Also WHITFIELD, G. and J., New York City. Pewter and britannia. No known examples.

WHITLOCK, JOHN H., Troy, New York, 1836-1844. Britannia. Common. He was a merchant who sold articles, stamped with his name, made by others.

Teapot	25.00
Coffee pot	40.00

Water pitcher, two quart, open   50.00
Water pitcher, lidded   75.00
*Bowl, 5½″ tall, shaped top
diameter 5⅛″, base 4⅛″. Engraved.   65.00
(Possibly a baptismal bowl, but more likely a waste bowl to a tea set.)

WHITMORE, JACOB, Middletown, Connecticut, 1758-1790. Plentiful.
in flatware. Whitmore and Thomas Danforth II, were contemporaries,
and were the first pewterers to work in Middletown, Connecticut. They
used molds owned jointly for most of their pewter.

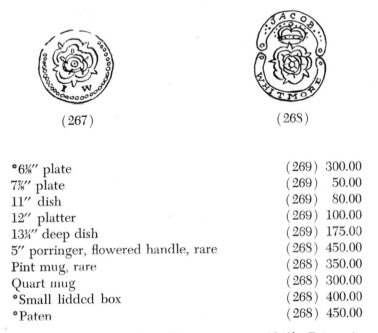

(267)   (268)

*6⅛″ plate	(269)	300.00
7⅞″ plate	(269)	50.00
11″ dish	(269)	80.00
12″ platter	(269)	100.00
13¼″ deep dish	(269)	175.00
5″ porringer, flowered handle, rare	(268)	450.00
Pint mug, rare	(268)	350.00
Quart mug	(268)	300.00
*Small lidded box	(268)	400.00
*Paten	(268)	450.00

WHITMORE, LEWIS, Rocky Hill, Connecticut, 1840's. Britannia.
No known examples.

WHITMORE and FRANCIS (—Whitmore and Daniel Francis), Buffalo,
New York, 1833-1835. Britannia.
No known examples.

WHITNEY
See BENHAM and WHITNEY.

*WILCOX, H. C. and COMPANY. (Horace C. and Dennis C. Wilcox), Meriden, Connecticut, 1850. Britannia. Rare. These two, together with I. C. Lewis, James Frary, L. J. Curtiss, W. W. Lyman, and John Munson, organized the Meriden Britannia Company in 1852. In 1898 the firm was incorporated into the International Silver Company.

> *Teapot   35.00

*WILDES (WILDS), THOMAS, Philadelphia, 1829-1833; New York City, 1833-1840. Britannia. Scarce.

> Candlesticks, 10″, pair   75.00
> Lamps, pair   85.00

WILL, GEORGE WASHINGTON, Philadelphia, 1798-1807. Possibly worked in Cincinnati later. The son of William Will. The touch shown, presumably that of this maker, is accompanied by the later touches of Blakslee Barns, who possibly stamped his touches some years after the plate was made by Will.

(269)

> 13¼″ deep dish, unique   350.00
> Syrup pitcher, late form, unique   200.00

WILL, HENRY, New York City, 1761-1775; 1783-1793; Albany, New York, 1775-1783. Very rare. As were his father (John) and brother (Wil-

Fig. 43: Two splendid tall flagons by Henry Will of Albany.

liam), Henry was a most gifted craftsman. Most of his flatware has a
hammered booge. His products are among the most desirable in American pewter.

(270)   (271)

(272)   (273)

(274)    (275)

8¾″ and 8⅞″-9¼″ plate	(270)	250.00	(271) 200.00	(273) 200.00
9⁷⁄₁₆″ plate	(271)	235.00	(272) 265.00	(273) 235.00
9″ plate, smooth brim	(270)	350.00	(271) 250.00	(273) 250.00
12⅜″-13³⁄₁₆″ platter	(271)	300.00	(272) 350.00	(273) 300.00
15″ platter	(271)	400.00	(272) 450.00	(273) 400.00
16⅜″ deep dish	(271)	600.00		
16½″ platter	(271)	600.00		
15¼″ x 11″ oval platter, extremely rare	(273)	2000.00		
6″ basin	(273)	350.00		
*8″ basin	(273)	275.00		
9½″ hot water plate, extremely rare	(273)	1000.00		
Pint mug	(273)	500.00	(275) 500.00	
Quart mug, two types	(273)	550.00		
*4¼″ porringer, Old English handle	(275)	650.00		
*4⅝″ beaker	(275)	650.00		
Quart tankard, dome top, crenate lip, two types	(273)	1400.00		
Quart tankard, flat top, crenate lip, three types	(271)	1500.00		
*Ladle	(271)	450.00		

Communion flagon	(273)	2000.00
Double lidded inkstand,		
unique	(273)	1500.00
Foot warmer, unique	(274)	1500.00
Tobacco box	(274)	1500.00

WILL, JOHN, New York City, 1752-1766. Extremely rare. This man was the father of Christian, Henry, John Jr., Philip, and William Will. His dates are very early for an American pewterer and his work is seldom found. His designs and his metal were of the highest order. His sons perhaps equalled him, but they never surpassed him in any way.

(276)

(277)

(278)

(279)

(280)

(281)

Fig. 44: A group of pieces by the Wills of New York and Philadelphia. Note the diversity of form and detail in hollow ware. Examples shown are by John Will, Sr., John Will, Jr., Henry Will, and Philip Will.
(Courtesy of William G. Goss, Jr.)

8″-8⁵⁄₁₆″
plate   (276)   550.00 (277)   500.00 (278) 500.00 (279) 500.00
*8⅞″ plate   (276)   600.00
9⅛″ plate   (276)   650.00 (279)   600.00
*13⅛″
deep dish   (276)   750.00 (279)   650.00
Pint mug   (280)   750.00
*Quart mug   (276)   850.00 (279)   800.00 (280) 800.00
Quart tankard, low double
dome top   (276) 1750.00 (280) 1750.00
Quart tankard, tulip shape; may be work of John
Will, Jr.   (280) 2000.00
3½″ pint mug, very
rare size   (280) 1500.00
3½″ pint tankard, very
rare size   (280) 2500.00
*Small creamer, two styles, one with footed, one with molded
base   (280)   700.00 (281)   800.00
Shaker   (276)   500.00
Beaker, 5¼″ (276)   800.00

WILL,, JOHN CHRISTIAN, New York City, 1770-1789. Son of John Will.
No known examples.

WILL, JOHN, JR., New York City, about 1750-1790.
See WILL, JOHN above.

WILL, PHILIP, Philadelphia, and New York City, 1763-1787.

(282)

*8″ plate, hammered booge   1000.00

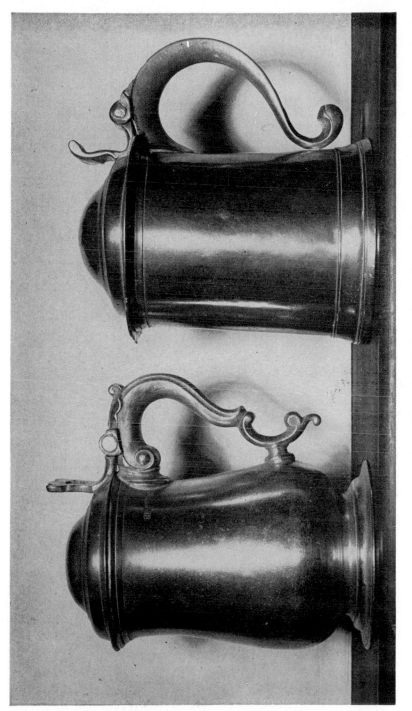

Fig. 45: *Tulip-shaped tankard with unusual double-C handle by John Will, Jr.; dome-top tankard with crenate lip by John Will, Sr.*

WILL, WILLIAM, Philadelphia, 1764-1798. Scarce. During his compara-
tively short career as a pewterer, interrupted by service to his country
and community during and after the War of Independence, Will turned
out pewter of the highest quality and individuality. New forms, unique
in American pewter, still come to light. His products are more eagerly
sought after than those of any other American pewterer.

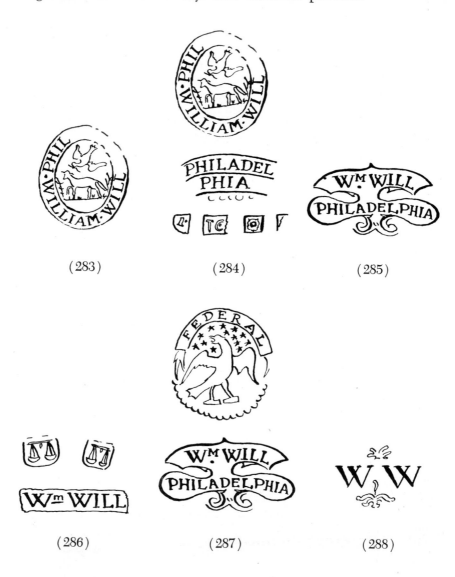

(283)   (284)   (285)

(286)   (287)   (288)

(289)

5⅜″ plate, smooth brim, name only	(286)	600.00		
*6⅛″ plate	(286)	600.00		
8″-8⅜″ plate	(287)	500.00		
*9¼″ hot water plate	(287)	1200.00		
9⅜″ plate, smooth brim	(287)	600.00		
12⅛″ platter	(287)	500.00	(289)	450.00
12¼″ deep dish	(289)	450.00		
16⅜″ platter, rare	(284)	800.00		
6½″ basin	(283)	500.00		
*10 5⁄16″ basin	(287)	600.00		
Teaspoon	(289)	250.00		
*Tablespoon	(289)	350.00		
12½″ ladle	(289)	600.00		
*Footed creamer	(288)	1000.00		
Pear-shaped teapot, early type	(286)	2750.00		
Pear-shaped teapot, footed	(285)	3500.00		
Baptismal bowl, 4⅛″ high, 8¾″ diameter (Lamb and dove touch only)	(284)	3500.00		
Teapot, drum-shaped	(289)	1500.00		
Coffee pot	(288)	5000.00		
*Water pitcher, mark unknown		1500.00		
*Chalice 7 15⁄16″, unmarked, found with marked flagon		500.00		
*Chalice, slightly different form, found with marked bowl		500.00		

*Ewer (pitcher), 9⅞", mark unknown	3000.00 or more			
*Ewer (pitcher), 10¾", unmarked, found with marked bowl	1200.00			
*Communion flagon, 13¹¹⁄₁₆", found with marked bowl	1200.00			
Communion flagon, 9¼", cylindrical		(286)	3500.00	
*8¾" baptismal bowl, mark unknown	2500.00			
*Small inkwell		(289)	850.00	
*Bed pan		(284)	650.00	(288) 650.00
*Commode form		(284)	650.00	
Pint mug		(286)	700.00	
Quart mug		(283)	800.00	(286) 750.00
Quart mug, tulip-shaped		(286)	800.00	(288) 750.00
Pint tankard		(286)	2500.00	
Quart tankard, dome top		(286)	1600.00	(288) 1500.00
Quart tankard, flat top		(286)	2000.00	
Quart tankard, tulip-shaped, two styles		(286)	1500.00	(288) 1500.00
*Candle-snuffer, unique in American pewter		(286)	1500.00	
*Spoon, unique in American pewter		(286)	600.00	

WILLETT, EDWARD, Upper Marlboro, Maryland; Charlestown, Maryland, 1692-1743. Extremely rare. A few plates, marked "EW Virginia" in a cartouche, cast on the under side of the brim, have been found and are correctly attributed to this maker. They are among the earliest known examples of American flatware.

*9⅛" plate, smooth brim   750.00

WILLETT, MARY, Upper Marlboro, Maryland, 1773.
No known examples.

WILLETT, WILLIAM, Upper Marlboro, Maryland, 1744-1772.
No known examples.

Fig. 46: Three Philadelphia tankards: the rare pint size by Cornelius Bradford; the two others by William Will.

Fig. 47: New York City and Albany pewter: the chalices are by Peter Young of Albany.

WILLIAMS, LORENZO, L., Philadelphia, 1838-1842. Britannia. Scarce.

Teapot	25.00
Sugar bowl	35.00
Creamer	35.00
*Baptismal bowl	125.00

WILLIAMS, OTIS, Buffalo, New York, 1826-1830. Son of Richard Williams (*see below*). Extremely rare.

(290)

8″ plate	600.00

WILLIAMS, RICHARD, Stepney, Connecticut, 1790's. One time partner of Thomas Danforth III, his father-in-law.
No known examples.

WILLIAMS and STIMPSON (Lorenzo L. Williams and Samuel Simpson), Yalesville, Connecticut, 1837-1838. Britannia. Rare.

Teapot	35.00

WILLIS, THOMAS, Philadelphia, 1829-1833.
No known examples.

WITHERLE (WEATHERLY), JOSHUA, Boston, 1784-1793.
No known examples.

WOLFE, JOHN, Philadelphia, 1801.
No known examples.

*WOOD, N. G., Boston area, about 1830. Very rare.

N.G.WOOD

(291)

3″ handled beaker   60.00

WOODBURY, J. B., Eastern Massachusetts or Rhode Island, late 1820's-1835; Philadelphia, 1835-?. Pewter and britannia. Scarce.

He was also in these partnerships: WHITEHOUSE and WOOD-BURY; WOODBURY and COLTON. The two eagle touches are worth a twenty-five percent premium, and his name touch with "PHILADa" is worth a fifteen percent premium.

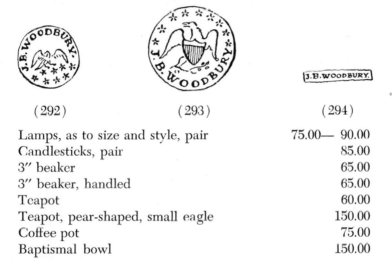

(292)   (293)   (294)

Lamps, as to size and style, pair	75.00— 90.00
Candlesticks, pair	85.00
3″ beaker	65.00
3″ beaker, handled	65.00
Teapot	60.00
Teapot, pear-shaped, small eagle	150.00
Coffee pot	75.00
Baptismal bowl	150.00

WOODMAN, COOK and COMPANY, Portland, Maine, 1840's. Britannia. Rare.

*Pint mug, late style   60.00

WYER, SIMON, Philadelphia, 1740-1752.
No known examples.

YALE, BURRAGE, South Reading, Massachusetts, 1808-1835. Pewter and britannia.
No known examples.

YALE, CHARLES, Wallingford, Connecticut, 1815-1824. Pewter and britannia. Rare.

Teapot   60.00

YALE, C. and S. (Charles and Selden Yale), Yalesville (Wallingford), Connecticut, 1817-1823.

YALE, CHARLES and COMPANY, same dates, locale as above.
No known examples by these partnerships. Though these men worked early enough to have made pewter, probably having an eagle touch, only britannia forms and name touches have been found. (*See also* YALE, HIRAM)

YALE, HIRAM, Wallingford, Connecticut, 1822-1831. Pewter and britannia. Scarce. (*See* YALE, H. and COMPANY.)

(295)

8⅜″ plate	90.00	
*11⅛″ deep dish	70.00	
*13″ deep dish	150.00	250.00 (combined with T. S. Derby touch)

13″ deep dish
*Teapot, pear-shaped   175.00

YALE, H. & CO., Yalesville, Connecticut, 1824-1835. Pewter, scarce; britannia, plentiful. Hiram and Charles Yale. Articles below are of britannia unless otherwise indicated.

(296)

11⅛″ deep dish, cast pewter	65.00
3″ beaker	45.00
3″ beaker, with unrecorded "Yale/Britannia" touch	65.00

Teapot	45.00
*Teapot, pear-shaped, cast pewter	150.00
Lighthouse coffee pot	60.00
7½″ chalices, pair	100.00
Communion flagon, 14″, unusually tall	125.00
*Two handled mug, cast pewter, unique form	350.00

YALE, W. and S., (William, Jr., and Samuel Yale), Meriden, Connecti
cut, 1813-1820. Very scarce. *William Yale, Sr., worked in Meriden, Connecticut, 1784-1810, and was a button maker only.

(297)

*6⅛″ plate	300.00
7⅞″ plate	125.00
8⅜″ plate	125.00
6″ basin	200.00
8″ basin	150.00

YALE and CURTIS (Henry Yale and Stephen Curtis), New York City,
1858-1867. Britannia. Rare.

Lamp, 1¼″, with two fonts drawing on single reservoir, unique	250.00
*Swivel lamp	60.00
Lamps, as to size and style, pair	75.00— 95.00

YOULE, GEORGE, New York City, 1793-1828. Extremely rare. The
ladle below is the only known example by this maker. Neither it nor
the touch have been previously recorded.

(298)

*14½″ ladle	450.00

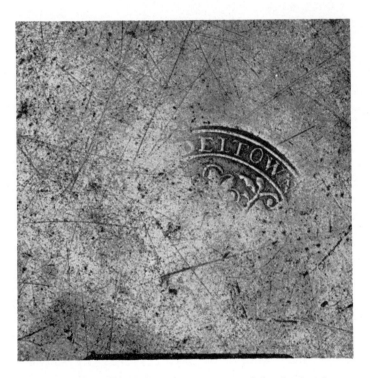

*Fig. 48: "Middletown" scroll touch used by both Thomas
Danforth II and Amos Treadway, Middletown, Conn.*

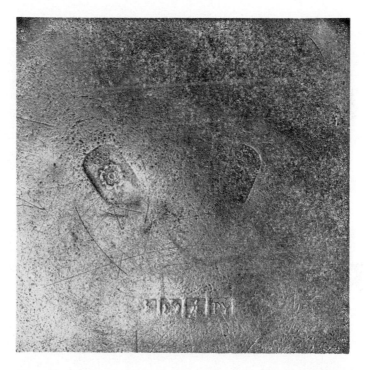

Fig. 49: Mark of Peter Young. Note that the initials follow the hallmarks rather than precede them. This is typical of English touches, but rare in American pewter.

YOULE, THOMAS, New York City, 1813-1819.
No known examples.

YOUNG, ABRAHAM, New York City, 1798-1801.
No known examples.

YOUNG, PETER, New York City, 1772-1782; Albany, New York, 1783-1800. Rare. Young was not just another pewterer. For quality of workmanship and originality of design, he ranks with Heyne, the Wills, and the Bassetts. Most of his flatware has hammered booges.

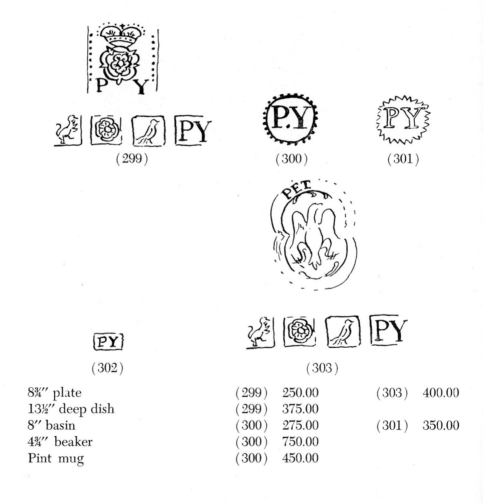

(299)

(300)

(301)

(302)

(303)

8¾″ plate	(299)	250.00	(303)	400.00
13½″ deep dish	(299)	375.00		
8″ basin	(300)	275.00	(301)	350.00
4¾″ beaker	(300)	750.00		
Pint mug	(300)	450.00		

Pint tankard, domed top,
very rare   (300) 2250.00
Quart tankard, flat top   (300) 1600.00
Flagon   (300) 1000.00
Chalices, pair   (300) 1200.00   (301) 1250.00
Footed creamer, 4⅞″   (302)   850.00

UNIDENTIFIED MARKS

Examples of unidentified eagle marks which occur on plates, basins, etc.

(304)

Found on a plate

(305)

Found on a basin

Appendix

The Danforths of Connecticut

Thomas Danforth I (1703-1786)
Worked in Taunton, Mass. 1727-33
and in Norwich, Conn. 1733-73.

m. (1) Sarah Leonard (1730)
m. (2) Hannah Hall (1742)

John Danforth (1741-1799)
of Norwich, Conn., and
Ellsworth, Ohio.
m. Elizabeth Hartshorn

Samuel (1772-1829)
of Norwich, Conn.
m. Lucy Hartshorn

John of Ellsworth, Ohio.

Thomas II (1731-82)
of Taunton, Mass., Norwich and
Middletown, Conn.
m. Martha Jacobs

Samuel (1774-1816)
of Hartford, Conn.
m. Melinda Seymour

Sarah Danforth
m. Oliver Boardman
of Litchfield, Conn.

Timothy Boardman
(1798-1825)
of Litchfield and
Hartford, Conn., and
New York.

William (1769-1820)
of Middletown, Conn.
m. Huldah Scovil

Sherman Boardman
(1787-1861)
of Litchfield and
Hartford, Conn.
m. Henrietta Richards

Henry S. Boardman
(Worked in Hartford,
Conn., and Philadelphia,
Pa., from 1841 to 1861)

Thomas Danforth Boardman
(1784-1873)
of Litchfield and
Hartford, Conn.
m. Elizabeth B. Lewis

Edward (1765-1830)
of Middletown
m. Jerusha Mossly

Josiah (1803-72)
of Middletown
m. Almira Camp

Joseph (1758-88)
of Middletown, Conn.
m. Sarah King

Joseph II (1783-1844)
of Middletown, Conn.
and Richmond, Va.

Thomas III (1756-1840)
of Middletown and
Stepney, Conn. and
Philadelphia, Pa.
m. Elizabeth Tallman

Thomas IV (1790-
1836) of Philadelphia,
Pa. and Augusta, Ga.

Hannah
m. Richard Williams
(1771-1812) of Wethers-
field, Stepney and Hart-
ford, Conn.

Otis Williams (1799-1831)
of Stepney and Hartford, Conn.
and Buffalo, N. Y.

Note: Job Danforth I of Taunton, Mass. was the nephew of
Thomas Danforth I and the father of Job Danforth II
(1774-1801) of Providence, R. I., who married Sally Barse.

The Danforths of Connecticut: Merchants Extraordinary

It seems appropriate to make special mention of the remarkable Danforth family and their school of pewterers because of the preponderance of their products from pre-revolutionary times to the end of the britannia period, when plating was introduced.

The chances are better than two to one that every piece of marked American pewter that turns up is the work of this school. It was their truly amazing merchandising ability, comparable to that of the tinsmiths and clock makers of Connecticut, that accounted for the immense success of the Danforths.

Thomas Danforth I, of Taunton, Massachusetts, and Norwich, Connecticut, and his descendants (including the Boardmans) and their trainees were predominant in the pewter trade for nearly a century. In general, the quality of their work was just average; for the most part they showed little individuality in creating distinctive forms. The emphasis was on readily salable standard items, with plates predominating.

Five or more generations of Danforth pewterers and their apprentices were turned out in such numbers that they were forced to expand west to Buffalo and to nearly every important pewtering center south to Georgia.

The greater part of the family came from the Connecticut River

*Fig. 50: Pewter by the Danforths and the Boardmans of Connecticut. Among
the outstanding forms are the following: Shelf 1—Tankard by Samuel Danforth
of Hartford, and dolphin-handled porringer by John Danforth of Norwich.
Shelf 2—A pair of transitional pear-shaped teapots, one by Samuel Danforth,
the other by Thomas Boardman; also shaker and small sugar bowl by Thomas
Danforth III. Shelf 3—Second from left—a lidless tankard by T. D. Boardman,
(a form which might well have been made from a mold originally belonging to
Thomas Danforth I). Shelf 4—The marked baluster measure and nursing bottle
are great rarities in American pewter. Both made by the Boardmans. Shelf 5—
A remarkable graduation of mugs by Samuel Danforth and the Boardmans.*

Valley. From Middletown, where Thomas Danforth II and Jacob Whitmore were the first pewter workers, starting in the 1750's, and from Hartford and Meriden, Danforth descendants, apprentices, and peddlers radiated in every direction. To Providence went Gershom Jones and Samuel Hamlin, both Danforth apprentices, who within a few years captured most of the market formerly held by the Newport pewterers: Benjamin Day, the Melvilles, the Belchers and others.

Otis Williams (great-great-grandson of Thomas I) went to Buffalo. Short-lived, he has left us only one plate bearing his marks. The Cincinnati area may yet yield an example by Williams or others of this school. South to Baltimore and Augusta went the Griswolds. Joseph Danforth, Jr., and Henry J. Danforth migrated to Richmond. Jacob Eggleston and William Nott went to Fayetteville, North Carolina.

To Philadelphia went Thomas Danforth III and Blakslee Barns, who were soon to confound the Philadelphia pewterers with their aggressive merchandising, producing within a few short years a volume which far eclipsed that of the native Philadelphians. Peddlers' carts were sent to every country crossroad—payment was taken in money, farm produce, scrap pewter, brass, or even broken glass, in early days. Hard workers and sharp traders indeed were these peddlers, some making fantastic profits. Many retired early in life after a few years' work, becoming either village "squires," or opening a bank, an importing, hardware, or other business.

A strange corollary to this success story is that we still have a great deal to learn about the early Danforth touches and their proper attributions. Are the oval lion touches with "T I" or "T D" really the work of the Norwich Danforths, Thomas I and his son John, as the three examples with the "Norwich" scroll would seem to indicate? If so, how do we explain the occurrence of these touches with the Middletown hallmarks of Thomas Danforth II? Did Thomas II bring this die to Middletown or inherit it from his father?

Dr. Laughlin mentions that Thomas Danforth II "died as peace was aborning." During the Revolutionary War Thomas was commissioned to gather pewter and lead scrap for ammunition. Presumably most of his pewter would be pre-revolutionary. How do we account for the very large amount of his work that has survived, compared to that of other pre-revolutionary pewterers? Did his son Thomas III make a great deal of that attributed to him? Are the small hallmarks and lion in circle touch really those of Thomas III or are they those of his father, Thomas II? What was Thomas III doing in the number of years that elapsed between his brief working period in Stepney, Connecticut, and his period of great production in Philadephia?

How do we account for the great number of pieces with the mark of Joseph Danforth? He worked only six years, in the 1780's. What was his son, Joseph, Junior, doing in the many years that preceded his brief career in Richmond? Is most of the pewter attributed to Joseph, Senior, that of his son with the father's touches?

These are some of the major riddles of American pewter still unsolved. Perhaps further research will shed light up on them.

Appendix

Characteristic Pewter Forms

(51a)   (51b)

(51c)   (51d)

Fig. 51: (a) Crown handle, New England and New York. (b) Conventional "Old English," New England and New York. (c) Flowered, Rhode Island and Connecticut. (d) Geometric, New England and New York.

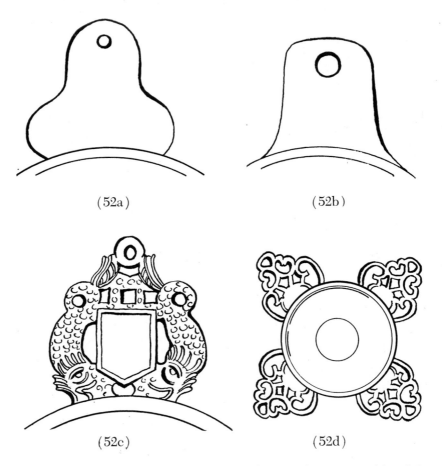

(52a)   (52b)

(52c)   (52d)

Fig. 52: (a) Solid, Rhode Island type. (b) Solid, Pennsylvania type. (c) Dolphin, New London and Hartford. (d) Lee-type four-handled basin, unique.

(53a)

(53b)   (53c)

Fig. 53: (a) Lee-type double-handled basin, unique. (b) Handle unique to Lee.
(c) Also unique to Lee.

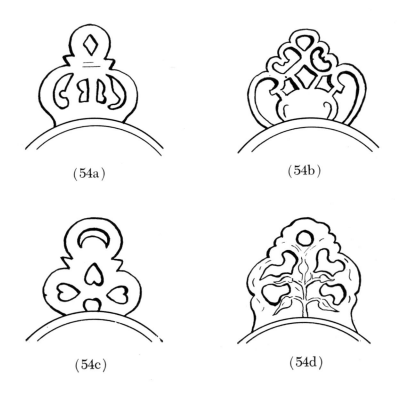

(54a)   (54b)

(54c)   (54d)

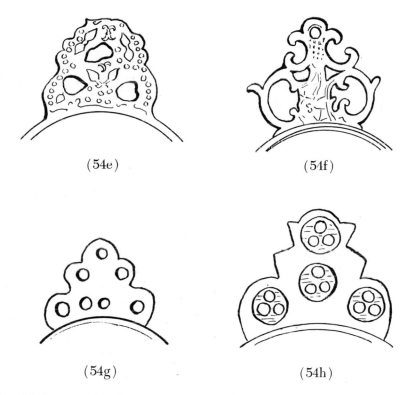

(54e)   (54f)

(54g)   (54h)

Fig. 54: Lee-type handles: (a) Also used by Boardman. (b) Unique to Lee. (c) Also used by Gleason. (d) Unique to Lee. (e) Also used by Isaac C. Lewis. (f) Unique to Lee. (g) Unique to Lee. (h) Unique to Lee, raised pattern.

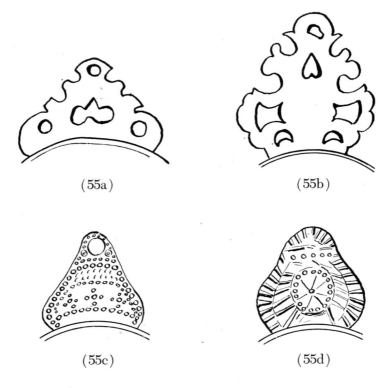

(55a)

(55b)

(55c)

(55d)

(55e)

(55f)

*Fig. 55: (a) Handle unique to Lee. (b) Boardman type. (c, d, and f) Lee types.
(e) New York type.*

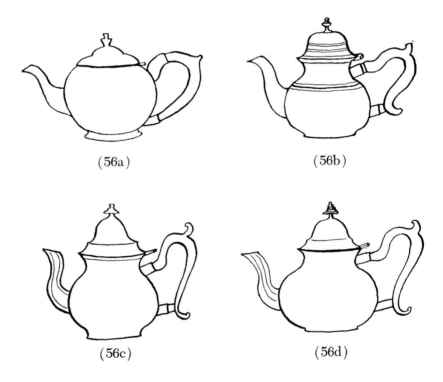

(56a)

(56b)

(56c)

(56d)

(56e)   (56f)

(56g)   (56h)

Fig. 56: Characteristic tea and coffee pot shapes: (a) Globular, Love bird touch.
(b) Pear-shaped; the Wills, Cornelius Bradford, and Brunstrom. (c) Rudi-
mentary foot on pear-shaped; Richardson and others. (d) Pear-shaped; William
Calder and others. (e) Footed pear-shaped; William Will and Cornelius Brad-
ford. (f) Federal style with feet; Israel Trask and others. (g and h) Federal
style, circular and oval; William Will, George Coldwell, Parks Boyd, and others.

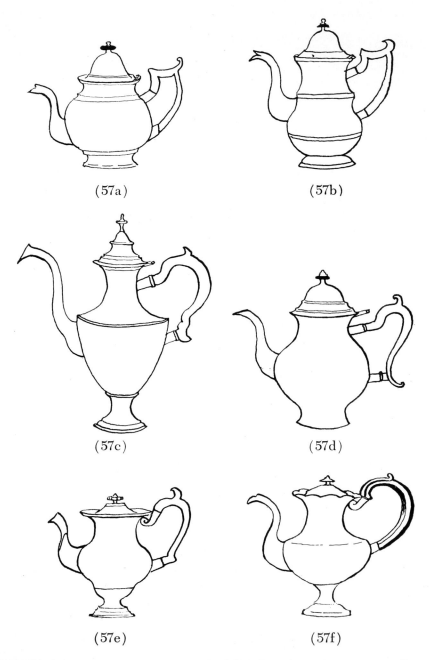

Fig. 57: (a) Pear-shaped, footed base, Richard Lee, Brunstrom and others. (b) Tall; many makers. (c) Coffee pot; William Will. (d) Tall; Samuel Danforth, Thomas D. Boardman, Samuel Kilbourn, and others. (e) Pigeon-breasted; Gleason and others. (f) Type from mid-nineteenth century; by Reed & Barton.